general biology

organisms, populations and ecosystems

BROWN

biology readings series

George E. Brosseau: *Evolution*

Reed A. Flickinger: *Developmental Biology*

Lester Goldstein: *Cell Biology*

Edward J. Kormondy: *General Biology, Volume I*

Edward J. Kormondy: *General Biology, Volume II*

Bradley Scheer: *Comparative Physiology*

Volume II

general biology

organisms, populations and ecosystems

Edward J. Kormondy, Ph.D.

Associate Professor of Biology
Oberlin College

WM. C. BROWN COMPANY PUBLISHERS
Dubuque, Iowa

Library of Congress Catalog Card Number: 66–24142

Manufactured by WM. C. BROWN CO., INC., Dubuque, Iowa
Printed in U. S. A.

preface

In developing this anthology, it was soon recognized that a single volume would severely circumscribe the diversity of biological literature. The ordering of subjects in the two volumes that resulted was based on the trend towards emphasizing one or two levels of biological organization in a one-semester introductory course. Thus, the first volume deals with the molecular and cellular levels of biological organization, the second with the levels of the organism and population, including the ecosystem.

As a science, biology should be so approached that the beginning student is made aware of its dynamic, inquiring character. It is the rare instructor who, charged with this responsibility, possesses the consummate skill needed to effectively convey this vitality of biology. It is, perhaps, too often the case that he is unable to convey this viable spirit, let alone to adequately discuss the skills of the myriad investigators who have brought biology to its present status. Descriptive textbook biology and descriptive teaching cannot accomplish this. Inquiry-oriented lectures and investigatory laboratories, coupled with direct confrontation with selected research literature, can provide the milieu for meaningful study. The use of such literature with beginning students has abundantly verified their ability to read it meaningfully and critically; there is no question of its efficacy. It adds a new and viable dimension to a course.

Few college libraries, however, have any significant historical depth in the biological literature. Many are indeed fortunate to have even a bare sampling of the broad spectrum of the current research literature. An anthology, such as this one, circumvents this library limitation while also accommodating the abundance required for larger classes.

The exigencies of space demanded by a reasonably-sized and -priced set of volumes precluded capricious abandon in the selection of papers and necessitated an *a priori* set of criteria for their choice. Foremost among these criteria was a paper bearing the approbation "classic" in the eyes of most biologists. Mendel's study on plant hybridization, Darwin's statement on speciation, and Vesalius' discourse on human anatomy are cases in point. Beyond the few truly outstanding accomplishments of biological research are those which have had significant influence on its direction – sometimes by clarifying, sometimes by challenging, or by placing a new perspective or insight. There is a sampling of such papers here, but many had to be omitted to allow for breadth of coverage. All the papers are excellent examples of the best scientific activity. The pervasive scientific qualities of these selections will derive cumulatively to the student who reads a substantial number; it will likely not come from any one.

The organization of papers is by "levels of organization." The disciplinary approach (anatomy, physiology, etc.) and the taxonomic approach (botany, zoology) appear increasingly inadequate in introducing biology, a matter which, however, is not properly debated here. According to a given disciplinary or taxonomic perspective, some strange bedfellows have arisen from this particular mode of presentation; other miscegenations, as comparably bizarre, would arise from alternate arrangements. It needs only to be said that no approach is without problems. Further, even if two authors had the same perspective, they would not be expected to develop the internal or sub-level arrangements used here, let alone to have selected or omitted given papers. Fortunately, a table of contents allows circumvention of the foibles of organization of any author.

I have deliberately avoided extended comment on each paper, confining my remarks to a very brief statement about each in the introduction to a section. While much can be said for placing a paper in its particular perspective by providing appropriate introductory remarks, much can also be said against discussing the meaning of the paper in some detail before it is read. This has too often been the case in source books. Let the student garner what he can from his own study, providing him beforehand with only the barest of essentials.

Another disposing reason to brief commentary was to be parsimonious in the use of space so that as much representation as possible might be included. Had long commentary been included, the spectrum of significant papers would have been foreshortened even more. To meet space exigencies, it was also necessary to edit and excerpt each paper; in so doing, I am hopeful the peculiar flavor of each paper has not been subserved.

Inasmuch as none of the "literature cited" sections of any paper are included, I deleted bibliographic references to a major extent. This has the unfortunate potential of creating a delusion that a given scientist worked in a vacuum, or that he was omniscient. The beginning student must be made well aware of the accretionary aspect of science and of the dependence of a given scientist on his predecessors and contemporaries.

Comments on the strengths and weaknesses of this set of readings will be most appreciated. Instructors and students who may use these selections can help improve the contents by sharing their critique with me.

I am grateful to the various authors and publishers whose permission enabled the compiling of these readings. Several colleagues, notably Anna Ruth Brummett and Tom K. Scott, both of Oberlin College, offered valuable criticism and suggestion; but, to no one can I lay blame for the particular elections and omissions which were eventually made. I have appreciated the use of the excellent resources of the Oberlin College Library and of its staff, especially Elizabeth Richards and Jo Ellen Flagg. My thanks to Cynthia Barrett Faulhaber, who translated several papers in German, and to Marie Cook for considerable typing. Finally, although actually foremost, this effort could not have taken place without a patient, forebearing wife who provided not only much editorial assistance but, more importantly, sustained understanding.

Edward J. Kormondy

introduction

The diversity of living things is scarcely more characteristic of biology than are the diverse approaches used in their study. For purposes of analysis, plants may be considered separately from animals (hence, botany and zoology), form as distinct from function (hence, morphology and physiology), genetics as distinct from adaptation (hence, the individual disciplines of genetics, evolution, etc.). Historically, biology has perceived its domain in just this way and has benefited immeasurably from such multiplicity of direction. However, there is a unity in biology which obtains because of or in spite of diversity, a unity which exists in the phenomenon of the living organism. It is this living entity which is the province of biology to probe, to ascertain its problems, and to seek their resolution.

Analytically, the organism, acellular or multicellular, may be resolved into cells of different structure and function arranged into systems having properties unique to themselves. These systems of cells may, in turn, be considered to be comprised of highly integrated molecular systems with properties and characteristics unique to each system. On the other hand, the organism may be considered as but one of a number of similar organisms, a population whose properties are unique to itself, and distinct and unpredicted from those of the organism itself. In turn, such populations can be analyzed as units interacting with each other and with their physico-chemical environment. Hence, a meaningful approach to the diversity of organisms as well as to their unity can be had by considering their levels of organization — at the level of the molecule, the cell, the organism, the population, and the ecosystem.

Such a hierarchy of organization provides for different levels of analysis and causal explanation of biological phenomena. A problem may be conceived or recognized at a given level; its ultimate resolution may be at another. Some biologists argue for explanation in terms of molecular mechanisms; others, while not denying the validity of such explanation, argue that the organism no longer exists at that level and seek for more holistic understanding at the other end of the spectrum. One might well argue that both points of view are requisite to a competent and complete understanding of biological systems at any level of organization.

Any dichotomy of subject matter runs the risk of implying structural as well as conceptual boundaries and barriers. This is not intended here; further, this should not be the case in biology. The organism is the same whether it is being looked at as an ordered array of electrons in peculiar molecular configurations or as an entity in a tide pool engaged in the recycling of an essential nutrient. It is not the organism but biologists who have dichotomized – it is they who are seldom of one mold by proclivity and by training. This has been fortunate for biological progress. The cross-fertilization and hybridization of different competences in many of the "traditional" disciplines of biology have yielded truly remarkable advances over the years.

Regardless of approach, there is an integrity and essence to biology which it is the challenge of an introductory course to convey. Lectures, demonstrations, and laboratories can accomplish a great deal towards this end provided they are soundly conceived and continually recognize the larger and long-range goals of the course. Increasing familiarity with the heritage of biological literature can also accomplish a great deal. It is in such literature that one begins to sense the ways in which biologists have come to know what they know – something of the nature of experimentation and observation, the patience required in investigation, the logic and creative aspects of their labors; in a word, the excitement of science.

The classic pieces of investigation which provided the mortar and limestone of today's scientific endeavor are admittedly passé and generally irrelevant to current research. They served a purpose in their day by directing an avenue of research, resolving or creating a problem, contributing to a now well-established concept. But, relevance to current investigation is not the purpose of reading classic studies. Their significance is in instruction by example and in attaining, although passively, a sense of the nature of the scientific process at the hands of those who have been part of it. In the truly great investigations, one finds the same demands as in today's "high-powered" research. Only the problems and techniques have changed; the *modus operandi* has not.

There is yet another facet of the nature of biology which should become increasingly and obviously apparent in studying these selections. Biological processes are enormously complex, the variables numerous and interrelated almost beyond conception. Resolving these complexities has involved increasing application of chemical and physical techniques and has led to increasing interpretation in mathematical models. These are hallmarks of mid-twentieth century biology. It is this very characteristic trend that calls for careful and continual circumspection of the substantive aspects of biology and the ordering of analytic tools into a proper perspective with respect to the whole of biology.

The increased application of the resources and sophisticated tools of other sciences has, in no small measure, revolutionized the thrust and conceptual organization of biology in recent years. However, this revolution could not have occurred without an increasingly sharpening focus on what the questions were which needed to be answered. This is one of the striking peculiarities of science – the progressive refinement of the question. It is with an orientation to seeing how some of the great questions of biology have been increasingly sharpened and tentatively resolved that these readings should be approached.

contents

ORGANISM LEVEL OF ORGANIZATION

ORGANISM LEVEL OF ORGANIZATION

Form and Function

At the organism level of analysis, the concern is with the intact organism, an organism that is typically considered as multicellular and/or multilayered. This level of biological organization has had the major focus of activity throughout much of the history of biology. To a very considerable extent the emphasis has been on morphology, the description of form. However, to decry all early biology as having been exclusively descriptive morphology would be inconsistent with the facts. Many of the early morphologists were also physiologists, at least in the sense of attempting to assign function to particular parts. Fewer such morphologists, however, were experimentally oriented in their study.

Perhaps the foremost "modern" morphologist was the sixteenth century's Andreas Vesalius whose anatomical discourse (p. 3) and exquisite illustrations are truly classic. Almost a century later, in 1628, William Harvey introduced quantification into the study of human form and function in analyzing the circulation of the blood (p. 6). The first notable plant anatomist was Nehemiah Grew (p. 9); Stephen Hales was the first experimental plant physiologist of consequence (p. 12). Morphological investigations were especially strong in the mid-nineteenth century; they are exemplified in the botanical studies of Hugo von Mohl (p. 19) and the zoological studies of Thomas Huxley (p. 29).

Experimental physiology took several major steps forward in the first half of the nineteeth century, concomitantly with the period of strong morphological emphasis. In the 1820s, the military physician William Beaumont conducted studies on the physiology of digestion by taking advantage of an unhealed wound which provided direct access to the stomach, an example *par excellence* of opportunism in science (p. 15). At the mid-point of the nineteenth century, Berthold initiated the field of experimental endocrinology by transplanting the testes in fowl (p. 22). At about the same time, Claude Bernard, often referred to as the "father of experimental physiology," introduced one of the most successful of experimental procedures, that of extirpation of the organ under study (p. 25).

Biochemical phenomena increasingly came under scrutiny following Bernard's pioneering work. Among the significant subsequent studies was that by Nuttall at the turn of the century in detecting antibody reactions in blood sera (p. 32). Otto Loewi, and subsequently H. H. Dale (p. 52), elucidated the role of specific biochemicals in the transmission of impulses across the nerve synapse; Loewi and Dale shared the Nobel Prize in medicine in 1936 for these studies.

An extensive sequence of papers on plant and animal internal secretions has extended from Berthold's hormone studies. In plants, for example, the studies by Boysen-Jensen in 1910 (p. 40) on auxins were followed by those of Went in 1927 (p. 43) and by Thimann and Skoog in 1933 (p. 46) and in 1957 by Brian and Hemming (p. 59). In animals, Bayliss and Starling (p. 36) demonstrated chemical rather than neural mediation of pancreatic secretion in 1902. Wigglesworth extended the phenomenon of chemical coordination to insects (p. 49), opening thereby a vast new area for scientific exploitation. Selye has proposed a more generally adaptive function to the internal secretions (p. 56).

The section ends with a paper by Zimmermann (p. 62) on an intriguing sampling procedure used in analyzing one of the most persistent problems in plant physiology – that of the transport of organic materials in the conducting tissues.

1

on the workings of the human body

ANDREAS VESALIUS

. . . But those who followed Galen, among whom I place Oribasius, Theophilus, the Arabs, and all our own writers whom I have read to date, all of them (and they must pardon me for saying this), if they handed on anything worth reading, borrowed it from him. And, believe me, the careful reader will discover that there is nothing they were further from attempting than the dissection of bodies. They placed an absolute trust in I know not what quality of the writing of their chief, and in the neglect of dissection of the rest, and shamefully reduced Galen to convenient summaries, never departing from him by so much as the breadth of a nail, that is supposing they succeed in arriving at his meaning. Nay, they place it in the forefront of their books that their own writings are pieced together from the teachings of Galen, and that all that is theirs is his. And so completely have all surrendered to his authority that no doctor has been found to declare that in the anatomical books of Galen even the slightest error has ever been found, much less could now be found; though all the time (apart from the fact that Galen frequently corrects himself, and in later books, after acquiring more experience, removes oversights that he had committed in earlier books, and sometimes teaches contradictory views) it is quite clear to us, from the revival of the art of dissection, from a painstakng perusal of the works of Galen, and from a restoration of them in several places, of which we

From the preface to *De Fabrica Corporis Humani*. Reprinted from the translation by B. Farrington with the publisher's permission from the Proceedings of the Royal Society of Medicine, Vol. 25 (1932), pp. 1357-1366.

have no reason to be ashamed, that Galen himself never dissected a human body lately dead. Nay more, deceived by his monkeys (although it is admitted that human bodies dried, and prepared as it were for an inspection of the bones, did come under his observation), he frequently wrongly controverts the ancient doctors who had trained themselves by dissecting human corpses. . . .

Thus in the First Book I have described the nature of all bones and cartilages, which, since the other parts are supported by them, and must be described in accordance with them, are the first to be known by students of anatomy. The Second Book treats of the ligaments by which the bones and cartilages are linked one with another, and then the muscles that affect the movements that depend upon our will. The Third comprises the close network of veins which carry to the muscles and bones and the other parts the ordinary blood by which they are nourished, and of arteries which control the mixture of Innate Heat and Vital Spirit. The Fourth treats of the branches not only of the nerves which convey the Animal Spirit to the muscles, but of all the other nerves as well. The Fifth explains the structure of the organs that subserve nutrition effected through food and drink; and furthermore, on account of the proximity of their position, it contains also the instruments designed by the Most High Creator for the propagation of the species. The Sixth is devoted to the heart, the *fomes* of the vital faculty, and the parts that subserve it. The Seventh describes the harmony between the structure of the brain and the organs of sense, without, however, repeating from the Fourth Book the description of the network of nerves arising from the brain. . . .

But here there comes into my mind the judgment of certain men who vehemently condemn the practice of setting before the eyes of students, as we do with the parts of plants, delineations, be they never so accurate, of the parts of the human body. These, they say, ought to be learned, not by pictures, but by careful dissection and examination of the things themselves. As if, forsooth, my object in adding to the text of my discourse images of the parts, which are most faithful, and which I wish could be free from the risk of being spoiled by the printers, was that students should rely upon them and refrain from dissecting bodies; whereas my practice has rather been to encourage students of medicine in every way I could to perform dissections with their own hands. Assuredly, if the practice of the ancients had lasted down to our day, namely, to train boys at home in carrying out dissections, just as in making their letters and in reading, I would gladly consent to our dispensing not only with pictures, but with all commentaries. For the ancients only began to write about dissection when they decided that honour demanded that they should communicate the art, not only to their children, but to strangers whom they respected for their virtue. For as soon as boys were no longer trained in dissection, the inevitable consequence at once followed that they learned anatomy less well, since the training had been abolished with which they had been wont to begin in youth. So much so that when the art had deserted the family of the Asclepiads and had been now for many centuries on the decline, books were needed to preserve a complete view of it. Yet how greatly pictures aid the understanding of these things, and how much more accurately they put the things before the eyes than even the clearest language, nobody can have failed to experience in geometry and the other mathematical disciplines . . . .

2

of the quantity of blood passing through the heart from the veins to the arteries; and of the circular movement of the blood

WILLIAM HARVEY

Thus far I have spoken of the passage of the blood from the veins into the arteries, and of the manner in which it is transmitted and distributed by the action of the heart; points to which some, moved either by the authority of *Galen* or *Columbus*, or the reasonings of others, will give in their adhesion. But what remains to be said upon the quantity and source of the blood which thus passes is of a character so novel and unheard-of that I not only fear injury to myself from the envy of a few, but I tremble lest I have mankind at large for my enemies, so much doth wont and custom become a second nature. Doctrine once sown strikes deeply its root, and respect for antiquity influences all men. Still the die is cast, and my trust is in my love of truth and the candour of cultivated minds. And sooth to say, when I surveyed my mass of evidence, whether derived from vivisections, and my various reflections on them, or from the study of the ventricles of the heart and the vessels that enter into and issue from them, the symmetry and size of these conduits – for Nature doing nothing in vain, would never have given them so large a relative size without a purpose – or from observing the arrangement and intimate structure of the valves in particular, and of the other parts of the heart in general, with many things besides, I frequently and seriously bethought me and long revolved in my mind, what might be the quantity of blood which was transmitted, in how short a time its passage

Reprinted from the translation of An anatomical dissertation upon the movement of the heart and blood in animals, being a statement of the discovery of the circulation of the blood, printed by G. Moreton, Canterbury, 1894.

might be effected, and the like. But not finding it possible that this could be supplied by the juices of the ingested ailment without the veins on the one hand becoming drained, and the arteries on the other getting ruptured through the excessive charge of blood, unless the blood should somehow find its way from the arteries into the veins, and so return to the right side of the heart; I began to think whether there might not be A MOVEMENT, AS IT WERE, IN A CIRCLE. Now this I afterwards found to be true; and I finally saw that the blood, forced by the action of the left ventricle into the arteries, was distributed to the body at large, and its several parts, in the same manner as it is sent through the lungs, impelled by the right ventricle into the pulmonary artery, and that it then passed through the veins and along the vena cava, and so round to the left ventricle in the manner already indicated. This movement we may be allowed to call circular, in the same way as *Aristotle* says that the air and the rain emulate the circular movement of the superior bodies; for the moist earth, warmed by the sun, evaporates; the vapours drawn upwards are condensed, and descending in the form of rain, moisten the earth again. By this arrangement are generations of living things produced; and in like manner are tempests and meteors engendered by the circular movement, and by the approach and recession of the sun.

And similarly does it come to pass in the body, through the movement of the blood, that the various parts are nourished, cherished, quickened by the warmer, more perfect, vaporous, spirituous, and, as I may say, alimentive blood; which, on the other hand, owing to its contact with these parts, becomes cooled, coagulated, and, so to speak, effete. It then returns to its sovereign the heart, as if to its source, or to the inmost home of the body, there to recover its state of excellence or perfection. Here it renews its fluidity, natural heat, and becomes powerful, fervid, a kind of treasury of life, and impregnated with spirits, it might be said with balsam. Thence it is again dispersed. All this depends on the movement and action of the heart.

The heart, consequently, is the beginning of life; the sun of the microcosm, even as the sun in his turn might well be designated the heart of the world; for it is the heart by whose virtue and pulse the blood is moved, perfected, and made nutrient, and is preserved from corruption and coagulation; it is the household divinity which, discharging its function, nourishes, cherishes, quickens the whole body, and is indeed the foundation of life, the source of all action. But of these things we shall speak more opportunely when we come to speculate upon the final cause of this movement of the heart.

Hence since the veins are the conduits and vessels that transport the blood, they are of two kinds, the cava and the aorta; and this not by reason of there being two sides of the body, as *Aristotle* has it, but because of the difference of office, not, as is commonly said, in consequence of any diversity of structure, for in many animals, as I have said, the vein does not differ from the artery in the thickness of its walls, but solely in virture of their distinct functions and uses. A vein and an artery, both styled veins by the ancients, and that not without reason, as *Galen* has remarked, for the artery is the vessel which carries the blood from the heart to the body at large, the vein of the present day bringing it back from the general system to the heart; the former is the conduit from, the latter the channel to, the heart; the latter contains the cruder, effete blood, rendered unfit for nutrition; the former transmits the digested, perfect, peculiarly nutritive fluid. . . .

3

of the seed in its state of vegetation

NEHEMIAH GREW

. . . If then we take a *bean* and dissect it, we shall find it cloathed with a doubled *vest* or *coat*. These *coats*, while the *bean* is yet green, are separable, and easily distinguished. Or in an old one, after it hath lay'n two or three days in a mellow soil; or been soaked as long a time in water. When 'tis dry, they cleave so closely together that the eye not before instructed will judge them but one; the inner *coat* (which is of the most rare contexture) so far shrinking up, as to seem only the roughness of the outer, somewhat resembling *wafers* under *maquaroons*.

The inner *coat*, in its natural state, is everywhere twice, and in some place, thrice as thick, as the outer. Next to the *radicle*, which I shall presently describe, it is six or seven times thicker; and encompasses the *radicle* round about . . . .

At the thicker end of the *bean*, in the outer *coat*, a very small *foramen* presents itself, even to the bare eye. In dissection 'tis found to terminate against the point of that *part* which I call the *radicle*. It is of that capacity, as to admit a small *virginal* wyer; and is most of all conspicuous in a green *bean*. Especially, if a little magnified with a good *spectacle*-glass. This *foramen* is not a hole casually made, or by the breaking off of the stalk; but designedly formed, for the uses hereafter mentioned. It may be observed not only in the great *garden bean*, but likewise in other *kinds*; . . .

Reprinted from The anatomy of plants begun with a general account of vegetation, founded thereupon, as printed by W. Rawlins, London, 1682.

That this *foramen* is truly permeable, even in old *setting beans,* and the other *seeds* above named, appears upon their being soaked for some time in water. For then, taking them out, and crushing them a little, many small bubbles will alternately arise and break upon it.

Of all *seeds* which have thick or hard *covers,* it is also observable, that they have the same likewise perforated, as above said, or in some other manner. And accordingly, although the *coats* of such seeds as are lodg'd in *shells* or *stones,* being thin, are not visibly *perforated;* yet the *stones* and *shells* themselves always are; . . .

The *coats* of the *bean* being stripp'd off, the proper *seed* shews itself. The parts whereof it is composed are three; the *Main Body,* and two more, appendant to it; which we may call the three *Organical Parts* of the *bean.*

The *Main Body* is not one entire piece, but always divided, lengthwise, into two halves or *lobes,* which are both joyn'd together at the *basis* of the *bean.* These *lobes* in dry *beans* are but difficultly separated or observ'd; but in young ones, especially boil'd, they easily slip asunder . . .

At the *basis* of the *bean,* the two other *Organical Parts* stand appendant; by mediation whereof, the two *lobes* meet and join together. The greater of these two *Parts* stands without the two *lobes,* and upon divesting the *bean* of its *coats,* is immediately visible. 'Tis of a white colour, and more glossie than the *Main Body,* especially when the *bean* is young. In the *bean,* and many other *seeds,* 'tis situated somewhat above the thicker end, as you hold the *bean* in its most proper posture for growth. . . .

The lesser of the two said appendents lies occult between the two *lobes* of the *bean,* by separation whereof only it is to be seen. 'Tis enclos'd in two small *cavities,* form'd in the *lobes* for its reception. Its colour comes near to that of the *radicle,* and it is founded upon the *basis* thereof, having a quite contrary production, towards the *cone* of the *bean;* as being that very *part,* which, in process, becomes the *body* or *trunk* of the *plant.* . . .

The general cause of the growth of a *bean,* or other *seed,* is *fermentation.* That is, the *bean,* lying in the mould, and a moderate access of some moisture, partly dissimilar and partly congenerous, being made, a gentle *fermentation* thence ariseth. By which, the *bean* swelling, and the *sap* still encreasing, and the *bean* continuing still to swell, the work thus proceeds: as is the usual way of explicating. But that there is simply a *fermentation,* and so a sufficient supply of *sap* is not enough: but that this *fermentation,* and the *sap* wherein 'tis made, should be under a various *government,* by divers *parts* thereto subservient, is also requisite;

and as the various preparation of the *aliment* in an *animal,* equally necessary: the particular process of the work according whereto, we find none undertaking to declare . . . .

4

experiments showing the quantities imbibed and perspired by plants and trees

STEPHEN HALES

July 3, 1724, in order to find out the quantity imbibed and perspired by the sunflower, I took a gardenpot with a large *sunflower,* 3 feet + 1/2 high, which was purposely planted in it when young; it was of the large annual kind.

I covered the pot with a plate of thin milled lead, and cemented all the joints fast, so as no vapour could pass, but only air, thro' a small glass tube, nine inches long, which was fixed purposely near the stem of the plant, to make a free communication with the outward air, and that under the leaden plate.

I cemented also another short glass tube into the plate, two inches long, and one inch in diameter. Thro' this tube I watered the plant and then stopped it up with a cork; I stopped up also the holes at the bottom of the pot with corks.

I weighed this pot and plant morning and evening, for fifteen several days, from *July* 3 to *Aug.* 8, after which I cut off the plant close to the leaden plate, and then covered the stump well with cement; and upon weighing found there perspired thro' the unglazed porous pot two ounces every twelve hours day; which being allowed in the daily weighing of the plant and pot, I found the greatest perspiration of twelve hours in a very warm dry day, to be one pound fourteen ounces; the middle rate of perspiration one pound four ounces. The perspiration of

Reprinted from Statical Essays: Containing Vegetable Staticks; or an account of some Statical Experiments on the Sap in Vegetables, Vol. 1, 3d. edition (1738).

a dry warm night, without any sensible dew, was about three ounces; but when any sensible, tho' small dew, then the perspiration was nothing; and when a large dew, or some little rain in the night, the plant and pot was increased in weight two or three ounces. N.B. *The weights I made use of were* avoirdupoise *weights.*

I cut off all the leaves of this plant and laid them in five several parcels, according to their several sizes; and then measured the surface of a leaf of each parcel, by laying over it a large lattice made with threads, in which the little squares were 1/4 of an inch each; by numbring of which I had the surface of the leaves in square inches, which multiplied by the number of the leaves in the corresponding parcels, gave me the area of all the leaves; by which means I found the surface of the whole plant, above ground, to be equal to 5616 square inches, or 39 square feet.

I dug up another sunflower, nearly of the same size, which had eight main roots, reaching fifteen inches deep and sideways from the stem: It had besides a very thick bush of lateral roots, from the eight main roots, which extended every way in a hemisphere, about nine inches from the stem and main roots.

In order to get an estimate of the length of all the roots, I took one of the main roots, with its laterals, and measured and weighed them; and then weighed the other seven roots, with their laterals; by which means I found the sum of the length of all the roots, to be no less than 1448 feet.

And supposing the periphery of these roots, at a medium, to be 0.131 of an inch, then their surface will be 2276 square inches, or 15.8 square feet; that is equal to 0.4 of the surface of the plant above ground.

If, as above, twenty ounces of water, at a medium, perspired in twelve hours day, (i.e.) thirty-four cubick inches of water, (a cubick inch of water weighing 254 grains), then the thirty-four cubick inches divided by the surface of all the roots is = 2286 square inches; (i.e.) $\frac{34}{2276}$ is $= \frac{1}{67}$; this gives the depth of water imbibed by the whole surface of the roots, *viz.* $\frac{1}{67}$ part of an inch.

And the surface of the plant above ground being 5616 square inches, by which dividing the 34 cubick inches, *viz.* $\frac{34}{5616} = \frac{1}{165}$, this gives the depth perspired by the whole surface of the plant above ground, *viz.* $\frac{1}{165}$ part of an inch.

Hence, the velocity with which water enters the surface of the roots to supply the expence of perspiration is to the velocity, with which their sap perspires, as 165 : 67, or as $\frac{1}{67} : \frac{1}{165}$, or nearly as 5 : 2.

The area of the transverse cut of the middle of the stem is a square inch; therefore the areas, on the surface of the leaves, the roots and stem, are 5616, 2276, 1.

The velocities, in the surface of the leaves, roots, and transverse cut of the stem, are gained by a reciprocal proportion of the surfaces.

$$\text{Area of}\left\{\begin{array}{lcr} \text{leaves} & = & 5616 \\ \text{roots} & = & 2276 \\ \text{stem} & = & 1 \end{array}\right| \text{velocity} \left| \begin{array}{l} = \frac{1}{5616} \\ = \frac{1}{2276} \\ = 1 \end{array}\right\} \text{or as} \left\{\begin{array}{l} \frac{1\text{ inch}}{165} \\ \frac{1\text{ inch}}{67} \\ 34\text{ inch} \end{array}\right.$$

Now, their perspiring 34 cubick inches in twelve hours day, there must so much pass thro' the stem in that time; and the velocity would be at the rate of 34 inches in twelve hours, if the stem were quite hollow . . . .

Having by many evident proofs in the foregoing experiments seen the great quantities of liquor that were imbibed and perspired by trees, I was desirous to try if I could get any of this perspiring matter; and in order to it, I took several glass chymical retorts and put the boughs of several sorts of trees, as they were growing with their leaves on, into the retorts, stopping up the mouth of the retorts with bladder. By this means I got several ounces of the perspiring matter of vines, ig trees, apple trees, cherry trees, apricot and peach trees; rue, horseradish, rheubarb, parsnip, and cabbage leaves; the liquor of all of them was very clear, nor could I discover any different taste in the several liquors: But if the retort stand exposed to the hot sun, the liquor will tast of the clodded leaves. Its specifick gravity was nearly the same with that of common water; nor did I find many air bubbles in it, when placed in the exhausted receiver, which I expected to have found; but when reserved in open viols, it stinks sooner than common water; an argument that it is not pure water; but has some heterogeneous mixtures with it.

I put also a large sunflower full-blown, and as it was growing, into the head of a glass still, and put its rostrum into a bottle, by which means there distilled a good quantity o liquor into the bottle. It will be very easy in the same manner to collect the perspirations of sweet-scented flowers, tho' the liquor will not long retain its grateful odor, but stink in a few days . . . .

5

experiments and observations on the gastric juice and the physiology of digestion

WILLIAM BEAUMONT

Whilst stationed at Michillimackinac, Michigan Territory, in 1822, in the military service of the United States, the following case of surgery came under my care and treatment.

Alexis St. Martin, who is the subject of these experiments, was a Canadian, of French descent, at the above-mentioned time about eighteen years of age, of good constitution, robust and healthy. He had been engaged in the service of the American Fur Company, as a voyageur, and was accidentally wounded by the discharge of a musket on the 6th of June, 1822 . . . .

I saw him in twenty-five or thirty minutes after the accident occurred, and, on examination, found a portion of the lung, as large as a turkey's egg, protruding through the external wound, lacerated and burnt; and immediately below this, another protrusion, which, on further examination, proved to be a portion of the stomach, lacerated through all its coats, and pouring out the food he had taken for his breakfast through an orifice large enough to admit the forefinger . . . .

After cleansing the wound from the charge and other extraneous matter and replacing the stomach and lungs as far as practicable, I applied the carbonated fermenting poultice and kept the surrounding parts constantly wet with a lotion of muriate of ammonia and vinegar; and gave internally the aq. acetam. with camphor, in liberal quantities.

Under this treatment a strong reaction took place in about twenty-four hours, accompanied with high arterial excitement, fever, and mark-

Reprinted from the book of the same name, published by F. P. Allen, Plattsburgh (1833).

ed symptoms of inflammation of the lining membranes of the chest and abdomen, great difficulty of breathing, and distressing cough.

He was bled to the amount of eighteen or twenty ounces and took a cathartic. The bleeding reduced the arterial action and gave relief. The cathartic had no effect, as it escaped from the stomach through the wound . . . .

After trying all the means in my power for eight or ten months to close the orifice, by exciting adhesive inflammation in the lips of the wound, without the least appearance of success, I gave it up as impracticable in any other way than that of incising and bringing them together by sutures; an operation to which the patient would not submit.

By the 6th of June, 1823, one year from the time of the accident, the injured parts were all sound, and firmly cicatrized, with the exception of the aperture in the stomach and side. This continued much in the same situation as it was six weeks after the wound was received. The perforation was about two and a half inches in circumference, and the food and drinks constantly exuded, unless prevented by a tent, compress and bandage . . . .

In the spring of 1824 he had perfectly recovered his natural health and strength; the aperture remained; and the surrounding wound was firmly cicatrized to its edges.

In the month of May, 1825, I commenced my first series of gastric experiments with him at Fort Mackinac, Michigan Territory. In the month of June following, I was ordered to Fort Niagara, N.Y., where, taking the man with me, I continued my experiments until August . . . .

He now entered my service, and I commenced another series of experiments on the stomach and gastric fluids, and continued them, interruptedly, until March, 1831. During this time, in the intervals of experimenting, he performed all the duties of a common servant, chopping wood, carrying burthens, &c., with little or no suffering or inconvenience from his wound. He laboured constantly, became the father of more children, and enjoyed as good health and as much vigour as men in general. He subsisted on crude food, in abundant quantities, except when on prescribed diet, for particular experimental purposes, and under special observance . . . .

Mode of Extracting the Gastric Juice. — The usual method of extracting the gastric juice, for experiment, is by placing the subject on his right side, depressing the valve within the aperture, introducing a gum-elastic tube, of the size of a large quill, five or six inches into the stomach, and then turning him on the left side, until the orifice becomes dependent. In health, and when free from food, the stomach is *usually* entirely empty and contracted upon itself. On introducing the tube, the fluid soon begins to flow, first by drops, then in an interrupted, and sometimes in a short continuous stream. Moving the tube about, up and down, or backwards and forwards, increases the discharge. The quantity of fluid ordinarily obtained is from four drachms to one and a half or two ounces, varying with the circumstances and condition of the stomach. Its extraction is generally attended by that peculiar sensation at the pit of the stomach, termed sinking, with some degree of faintness, which renders it necessary to stop the operation. The usual time of extracting the juice is early in the morning, before he has eaten, when the stomach is empty and clean . . . .

Experiment 1

August 1, 1825. At 12 o'clock, M., I introduced through the perforation, into the stomach, the following articles of diet, suspended by a silk string, and fastened at proper distances, so as to pass in without pain—viz. : —a piece of high-seasoned *a la mode beef;* a piece of *raw, salted, fat pork,* a piece of *raw, salted, lean beef;* a piece of *boiled, salted beef;* a piece of *stale bread;* and a bunch of *raw, sliced cabbage;* each piece weighing about two drachms; the lad continuing his usual employment about the house.

At 1 o'clock, P.M., withdrew and examined them—found the *cabbage* and *bread* about half digested: the pieces of *meat* unchanged. Returned them into the stomach.

At 2 o'clock, P.M., withdrew them again—found the *cabbage, bread, pork,* and *boiled beef* all cleanly digested, and gone from the string; the other pieces of meat but very little affected. Returned them into the stomach again.

At 2 o'clock, P.M., examined again—found the *a la mode beef* partly digested: the *raw beef* was slightly macerated on the surface, but its general texture was firm and entire. The smell and taste of the fluids of the stomach were slightly rancid; and the boy complained of some pain and uneasiness at the breast. Returned them again . . . .

This experiment cannot be considered a fair test of the powers of the gastric juice. The cabbage, one of the articles which was, in this instance, most speedily dissolved, was cut into small, fibrous pieces, very thin, and necessarily exposed on all its surfaces, to the action of the gastric juice. The stale bread was porous, and, of course, admitted the juice into all its interstices; and probably fell from the string as soon as softened, and before it was completely dissolved. These circumstances will account for the more rapid disappearance of these substances, than of the pieces of meat, which were in entire solid pieces when put in. To account for the disappearance of the fat pork, it is only necessary to remark that the fat of meat is always resolved into oil by the warmth of the stomach before it is digested. I have generally observed that when he has fed on fat meat or butter, the whole superior portion of the contents of the stomach, if examined a short time after eating, will be found covered with an oily pellicle. This fact may account for the disappearance of the pork from the string. I think, upon the whole, and subsequent experiments have confirmed the opinion, that fat meats are less easily digested than lean, when both have received the same advantages of comminution. Generally speaking, the looser the texture, and the more tender the fibre, of animal food, the easier it is of digestion.

This experiment is important, in a pathological point of view. It confirms the opinion that undigested portions of food in the stomach produce all the phenomena of fever; and is calculated to warn us of the danger of all excesses where that organ is concerned. It also admonishes us of the necessity of a perfect comminution of the articles of diet.

6

course of the vascular bundles in the stem

HUGO von MOHL

Before I proceed to the microscopic anatomical description of the stem, it will be necessary to describe the course of the vascular bundles. It is known that these do not lie in concentric circles, but are scattered without definite arrangement throughout the stem. This difference of the palms from dicotyledonous trees is so striking that even in ancient times it was regarded as a characteristic peculiarity of palms. The course of the vascular bundle is best traced in stems where the parenchyma has lost its firmness by decomposition; in these the individual bundles may with very little trouble be extricated from a stem split longitudinally. Stems with a white pith-like centre are also very well adapted to this investigation. When, in such a stem, e.g. *Kunthia montana,* a vascular bundle is traced from the point of insertion of the leaf backward, it is found that it runs in a curve (the convexity upward) to the centre of the stem, then in the neighbourhood of the centre runs down a certain extent deep in the stem, but soon again loses the direction parallel to the axis of the stem, gradually (since at the same time it is always running down the stem) again approaching the surface, till it lies beneath the rind, and there passes down the stem beneath this.

Obs. I have here described the course of the vascular bundle in the direction from above downward, because I usually traced them in this direction in the stem; but it must not be hence inferred that the vascu-

Reprinted from On the structure of the palm stem, Vermischte Schriften botanischen Inhalts, Tübingen, 1845 as translated by Arthur Henfrey in Reports and Papers on Botany, The Ray Society, London (1849).

lar bundle of palms is perfected in this direction in its formation; and in the following pages I shall, according as it may be more conveniently stated, follow the vascular bundle, in the anatomical description, sometimes from above downward, and sometimes in the opposite direction.

The course of the vascular bundle is the same in all palms, and the only distinctions which present themselves are a difference of aspect at different points of the course of the vascular bundle in different species.

In those species, for instance, which, like *Kunthia montana* and *Mauritia aculeata,* possess firm woody vascular bundles only at the periphery of the stem, with a centre composed of soft, herbaceous substance, we find that all the bundles are thin, soft, and herbaceous from the point where they enter the leaf downward to the centre of the stem, and from here outwards to the point where they approach the outer hard, woody layer, and that as they proceed downward in their course in that layer, they gradually become denser and of a firm ligneous consistence. When the vascular bundles have reached the external part of this layer and become situated beneath the rind, their thickness is diminished, but not their firmness and hardness; the latter peculiarity, however, is less remarkable on account of their smaller diameter. They run in this manner, in the form of slender fibres, between the firm, woody layer and the rind, to the base of the stem, or terminate, after a course of variable length, in other vascular bundles, becoming blended with them. As all the vascular bundles have a similar course, and the portion running in the middle of the stem is soft and herbaceous in all, the medulla-like softness of the centre of the stems is easily explained. It is also clear that the hardness of the outer layer of the stem results from the thickness and solidity acquired by the collective vascular bundles during their course through this outer layer; further, that the liber-like fibrous layer under the rind is formed by the lower extremities of the vascular bundles, and is not to be compared with the liber of dicotyledons.

The vascular bundles of the *Cocos*- and *Calamus*-like stems are distinguished by their not exhibiting that herbaceous softness in their course from the leaf to the centre, and from this to the outer layer of the stem, for they also appear thick and woody here, although in a less degree than in the outer layers. With regard to the inferior portion of the vascular bundle, two varieties are met with in the *Cocos*-like stem: it either passes, as in *Kunthia,* into a thin fibre, and the external fibrous layer of the stem is then thin, as in the rest of the forms, or the vascular bundle divides, at its exit from the hard layer, into several smaller bundles, which, after a short course, lose themselves in a multitude of fine fibres; the fibrous layer is then thick, as, for instance, in *Cocos nucifera, coronata,* &c.

From this course of the vascular bundle is deduced the following statement: *The doctrine laid down by* Desfontaines *that the new vascular bundles originate in the centre of the stem, and that the harder and thicker vascular bundles, situated at the periphery of the stem, are older than the soft ones occupying the centre, and that, therefore, the vegetation of monocotyledons is wholly different from that of dicotyledons is altogether incorrect and inadmissible.*

Obs. 1. From the circumstance that the vascular bundles run from the leaves to the middle of the stem in a curve of small radius, but that from here, in their way downward, they only approach the rind gradually, we can understand how phytotomists have been led to assume that they originate in the middle of the stem. Indeed, this outward course is not easily observed in a stem split longitudinally, unless the single vascular bundle is dissected out. One circumstance, however, must have long since indicated the incorrectness of Desfontaines' doctrine. If, namely, the vascular bundles of the younger leaves lay more internally in the stem than those which go to the older leaves, the former could never cross the latter. Now, it is easily seen in all palms that the vascular bundles entering a leaf cross those which run to the leaves situated higher up, which is only possible by the arangement of the fibres described above. This crossing is the more striking the thicker the stem and the closer its leaves, therefore much more evident in the species of *Cocos* than in *Kunthia;* it is still more distinct in *Xanthorrhoea hastilis* (vide De Candolle, Organogr. tab. 7, 8), in a transverse section of the stem of which the vascular bundles entering the leaves have the aspect of medullary rays. The crossing is also very evident in the stem of *Pandanus, Dracæna, Draco, Aletris fragrans, Aloë, Bambusa,* &c.

Obs. 2. The smaller diameter of the lower liber-like end of the vascular bundles simply explains the less degree of thickness of the fibrous layer of the stem. Where each vascular bundle ends in a single filament, as in *Bactris, Geonoma, Lepidocaryum, Calamus, Kunthia, Ænocarpus, Hyospathe, Rhapis,* &c., this layer is very thin; when, on the other hand, the vascular bundle gives off several fibres, or when, as in *Mauritia vinifera,* the fibres retain a considerable thickness, the thickness of the fibrous layer is not altogether inconsiderable. I found it in *Leopoldinia pulchra* from 1/2 to 2 lines; in *Syagrus cocoides* 1 line; in *Cocos nucifera, Euterpe edulis, Mauritia vinifera,* 6 lines thick. . . . .

7

transplantation of the testes

A. A. BERTHOLD

On August 2 of last year, I castrated six young cockerels; namely a, b, and c of 2 months and d, e, f of three months. None of the wattles, combs and spurs were taken from any of these birds. Both testes were taken from a and d; these animals later showed completely the nature of capons, acted cowardly, entered only seldom into a short, half-hearted fight with other cockerels, and uttered the well-known monotone sounds of the capon. The comb and wattle turned pale and developed only somewhat; the head remained small. When these birds were killed on December 20, a meaningless, hardly noticeable scar was located where the testes had been. The spermatic duct was recognizable as a thin, delicate fibre.

B and e were castrated in the same way; however, only one testis was removed from the body, leaving the other isolated in the abdominal cavity. On the other hand, both testes were extracted from c and f, inserting one testis from cockerel f into cockerel c, and one testis from cockerel c into cockerel f between the intestines.

These four cockerels displayed in their general behavior the nature of uncastrated animals; they crowed quite suitably; they were often involved in fights among each other and with other young cockerels; and they displayed the usual interest in hens; their combs and wattles developed like those of normal cockerels.

Reprinted from the Archiv für Anatomie, Physiologie und Wissenschaftliche Medicin, 1849, pp. 42-46.

Cockerel b was killed on October 4. The one testis had healed onto the original place, had gained more than one half in circumference, was furnished with numerous blood vessels, showed clearly the seminal tubules, and gave out a whitish liquid supplied with larger and smaller cells, which, however, did not show any spermatazoids.

The fairly well-developed combs and the wattles were cut off of cockerels c, e, and f on the same day, and the abdominal cavities were opened in order to study the testes. In cockerel e, I found the testes in the usual place as in the dead cockerel b; I cut this testis and took it from the abdominal cavity and found it constituted just like the testis from b. The abdominal wound healed quickly; comb and wattle scabbed over but did not grow back. Instead of the earlier kind of crowing, the bird emitted the known tones of the capon; it was no longer interested in hens nor did it fight with the other cockerels; in fact, it distanced itself from them and showed now mainly the personality of a true capon.

With cockerels c and f no trace of the testes was found where these had been. The combs and wattles grew back; the animals retained their male personality, crowed as before, and maintained their earlier behavior toward hens and other cockerels. These two cockerels were killed on January 30, 1849. In the place of the testes no trace of the testes was to be found; on the contrary, the testis in c was found on the side of the colon, away from the back, and bordered on both sides by the end of the caecum without having grown into the latter. In cockerel f the same results occurred except that the position of the growth was somewhat more to the back, towards the middle of the caecum. The testes in both were oval-shaped, length 15, width 8 and depth 6 lines. Strong protuberances of the mesenteric vessels occurred here, and in many places they forced their way into the inside of the testes and were traceable to the seminal tubes. When I cut the testes open, a white milky liquid flowed out which had completely the conditions and the smell of normal cockerel semen. Under the microscope I detected numerous larger and smaller cells (1/450-1/550 lines in diameter) in the liquid and also numerous spermatazoids with the finest vibratile movements which became much more energetic when mixed with a drop of water.

From these experiments comes the following general results for physiology:

1. The testes belong to the transplantable organs; they heal up again after they have been removed from the body; in fact, they can be transplanted from one individual to another and the healing process occurs both where the testes have been removed and also in a completely strange place, namely on the walls of the intestines.

2. The transplanted testes continue to grow, even in a completely different location, in its special qualities as a semen organ; the seminal tubules expand and grow larger and carry out their normal function by secreting a completely normal semen characterized by spermatazoids. We find here the same condition as in plants where the scion continues to grow in its specific way on the parent stock and brings fruit not of the parent stock but in relation to itself.

3. It is a known fact that severed nerves grow back together and that in parts, the nerves of which have been severed, sensitivity and movement return after the healing. It often happens in the healing of a transplanted skin graft onto another part of the body that the nerve fibers which belong together cannot unite. However, it happened in the healing of the severed testes to completely different parts of the body, namely to the caecum, whereby the testes continues to develop as a semen producing organ and prepares real semen, that there are no specific semen nerves; and this is a major argument against the assumption of certain trophic nerves which the sympathetic nerve system had been held to be, even into most recent times.

4. The interesting consensual and antagonistic relationship between the life of the individual and of the species, as especially occurs during puberty and lasts until advanced age, is also not lacking, even if the testes are removed from their original place and their nerves grafted onto a completely new part of the body. In respect to voice, reproductive desire, bellicosity, growth of the combs and wattles, these animals remain real cockerels. Since, however, transplanted testes cannot be connected with their original nerves, and since there are no specific nerves controlling secretion, as illustrated in the third section, it follows therefore that the questionable consensus is limited by the productive condition of the testes, i.e., by their effect on the blood and via respective effect of the blood on the general organism, of which the nerve system represents at any rate a substantial part.

8

on the mechanism of formation of sugar in the liver

CLAUDE BERNARD

The glycogenic function of the liver is one of the things which has had the privilege of attracting the attention of physiologists, chemists, and physicians most intensely because of the importance of the ideas it raises in general physiology.

After establishing the universality of the new function by numerous experiments on men and animals, studying it under physiological conditions and localizing it in the liver, I was obliged to consider penetrating farther into the phenomenon, to try to fathom the intimate mechanism of sugar production in animals . . . .

MECHANISM OF THE GLYCOGENIC FUNCTION OF THE LIVER

All secretions necessarily require two things, namely: 1. blood; 2. glandular tissue. We shall be obliged to seek to assess what the respective role of each of these components is in the production of sugar. . . .

The hypotheses on the formation of sugar in the urine which I have recalled for you, all express the idea that is generally made today about the mechanism of secretions. It is thought, in effect, that the glandular organ does not supply anything to the secretion, but that its tissue is limited to act by a kind of contact or catalytic action on the elements in the blood which traverse the glandular organ at the same moment when

Reprinted from Comptes-Rendus des Séances de l'Académie des Sciences, Vol. 41 (1855), pp. 461-469. Translated by Edward J. Kormondy, 1965.

the secretion takes place. In the particular case of the secretion of sugar in the liver, we have seen, in effect, that all authors suppose the sugary material to be formed *directly* in the blood.

The facts which I have to reveal actually seem to me of such nature as to prove that the glycogenic function of the liver must be comprehended quite otherwise, and that in lieu of seeking *in the blood* the substance which precedes sugar and which there gives its immediate origin, one must search *in the hepatic tissue* itself.

Here is an experiment which I have conducted and which sheds some light on this fact; I shall describe it in some detail, so that one may easily reproduce the results which seemed very important to me and worthy of interesting the time of physiologists and chemists.

I chose an adult dog, vigorous and in good health, which was fed for several days exclusively on meat, and I sacrificed it by sectioning the medulla seven hours after a copious repast of tripe. The abdomen was immediately opened; the liver was removed avoiding injury to its tissue, and the organ still warm and before the blood had time to coagulate in the vessels was subjected to a wash of cold water through the portal vein. For this, I took a tube of gutta percha about one meter long with copper delivery tubes at its two ends. The tube, previously filled with water, had one of its ends firmly applied on the trunk of the portal vein at its entrance to the liver, and the other attached to the spigot of the spring of the College of France's medical laboratory. Upon opening the spigot, the water traversed the liver with great rapidity, for the force of the water current was capable, as measured, to raise a column of mercury to a height of 127 cm. Under the influence of this energetic lavage, the liver swelled, the color of its tissue paled, and the blood was flushed with the water which escaped in a strong continuous jet through the hepatic veins. At the end of about a quarter of an hour the liver tissue was nearly bloodless, and the water which left by the hepatic veins was entirely colorless. I left this liver under the continuous lavage for 40 minutes without interruption. I had established at the beginning of the experiment that the red-colored water which spurted from the hepatic veins was sweet and precipitated abundantly upon heating, and I determined at the end of the experiment that the perfectly colorless water which left the hepatic veins contained not the slightest trace of either albuminous material nor sugar.

Then the liver was removed and the action of the current withdrawn; and I assured myself by boiling a piece with a little water that its tissue was well washed since it no longer contained any sugary material. Its decoction gave no indication of reducing copper-potassium liquid nor any trace of fermentation with the yeast of beer. There escaped from the cut of the hepatic tissue and the gaping vessels a small quantity of a cloudy liquid which also contained no trace of sugary material. I then left the liver in a jar at ambient temperature, and on returning 24 hours later, I determined that this organ, well washed of its blood and which I had left completely deprived of sugar the day before, was found to be very abundantly provided with sugar. It sufficed to convince me upon examining a little of the liquid which had drained out of the liver and finding it exceedingly sweet; then, on injecting cold water with a small syringe by way of the portal vein and collecting this water when it left by the hepatic veins, I determined that this liquid gave instead, with the yeast of beer, a very bountiful and active fermentation.

This experiment, so simple, in which one can see before his very eyes sugary material reappear in a liver which had been completely freed of it along with its blood by the lavage method, is one of the most decisive for the solution of the glycogenic function which concerns us. This experiment proves clearly, as we have previously advanced, that within a fresh liver in the physiological, i.e., the functional, state, there are two substances, namely: 1. sugar, very soluble in water and which is removed with the blood by lavage; 2. another substance so slightly soluble in water that it remains bound to the hepatic tissue after the latter has been stripped of its sugar and of its blood by a 40-minute washing. It is this lattermost substance which, in the liver left to itself, is changed slowly into sugar by a kind of fermentation, as we will demonstrate. . . .

In conclusion the only purpose of my work for the moment is to prove that the sugar which is formed in the liver is not produced *at once* in the blood, if I may be permitted to express myself in that way, but that its presence is always preceded by a special substance, deposited in the liver tissue, which gives rise to it immediately. If I have decided to publish this still incomplete study, it is because it seemed advantageous for the solution of the glycogenic question which is before us to attract the attention of chemists in these phenomena which are unknown to them and which seem to me of such a nature as to change the point of view from which there has been based until now a chemical understanding of the production of sugar in the liver. In effect, it is no longer a question of making hypotheses on the production of sugar in the liver nor on the possibility of direct and immediate decomposition of this or that component of blood to produce this sugar. It is necessary to try to isolate this singular hepatic material which precedes it to know how it is secreted in the liver, and how it subsequently undergoes the successive transformations which change it into sugar.

Probably between these two extremes, the insoluble material just as it secreted by the vital action of the liver and the sugar which emanates and leaves the organ with the blood of the hepatic veins, there is a series of intermediate steps which I have not seen, but which chemists will doubtless discover.

9

a lobster; or, the study of zoology

THOMAS H. HUXLEY

I have before me a lobster. When I examine it, what appears to be the most striking character it presents? Why, I observe that this part which we call the tail of the lobster is made up of six distinct hard rings and a seventh terminal piece. If I separate one of the middle rings, say the third, I find it carries upon its undersurface a pair of limbs or appendages, each of which consists of a stalk and two terminal pieces, so that I can represent a transverse section of the ring and its appendages upon the diagram board in this way.

If I now take the fourth ring, I find it has the same structure, and so have the fifth and the second; so that, in each of these divisions of the tail, I find parts which correspond with one another, a ring and two appendages; and in each appendage a stalk and two end pieces. These corresponding parts are called, in the technical language of anatomy, "homologous parts." The ring of the third division is the "homologue" of the ring of the fifth, the appendage of the former is the homologue of the appendage of the latter. And, as each division exhibits corresponding parts in corresponding places, we say that all the divisions are constructed upon the same plan. But now let us consider the sixth division. It is similar to, and yet different from, the others. The ring is essentially the same as in the other divisions; but the appendages look at first as if they were very different; and yet when we regard them closely, what do

Reprinted from a lecture delivered at the South Kensington Museum as reproduced in Discourses: Biological and Geological Essays, Appleton and Co., New York (1894).

we find? A stalk and two terminal divisions, exactly as in the others, but the stalk is very short and very thick, the terminal divisions are very broad and flat, and one of them is divided into two pieces.

I may say, therefore, that the sixth segment is like the others in plan, but that it is modified in its details.

The first segment is like the others, so far as its ring is concerned, and though its appendages differ from any of those yet examined in the simplicity of their structure, parts corresponding with the stem and one of the divisions of the appendages of the other segments can be readily discerned in them.

Thus it appears that the lobster's tail is composed of a series of segments which are fundamentally similar, though each presents peculiar modifications of the plan common to all. But when I turn to the forepart of the body I see, at first, nothing but a great shield-like shell, called technically the "carapace," ending in front in a sharp spine, on either side of which are the curious compound eyes, set upon the ends of stout movable stalks. Behind these, on the underside of the body, are two pairs of long feelers, or antennae, followed by six pairs of jaws folded against one another over the mouth, and five pairs of legs, the foremost of these being the great pinchers, or claws, of the lobster.

It looks, at first, a little hopeless to attempt to find in this complex mass a series of rings, each with its pair of appendages, such as I have shown you in the abdomen, and yet it is not difficult to demonstrate their existence. Strip off the legs, and you will find that each pair is attached to a very definite segment of the underwall of the body; but these segments, instead of being the lower part of free rings, as in the tail, are such parts of rings which are all solidly united and bound together; and the like is true of the jaws, the feelers, and the eyestalks, every pair of which is borne upon its own special segment. Thus the conclusion is gradually forced upon us, that the body of the lcbster is composed of as many rings as there are pairs of appendages, namely, twenty in all, but that the six hindmost rings remain free and movable, while the fourteen front rings become firmly soldered together, their backs forming one continuous shield—the carapace.

Unity of plan, diversity in execution, is the lesson taught by the study of the rings of the body, and the same instruction is given still more emphatically by the appendages. If I examine the outermost jaw I find it consists of three distinct portions, an inner, a middle, and an outer, mounted upon a common stem; and if I compare this jaw with the legs behind it, or the jaws in front of it, I find it quite easy to see, that, in the legs, it is the part of the appendage which corresponds with the inner division, which becomes modified into what we know familiarly as the "leg," while the middle division disappears, and the outer division is hidden under the carapace. Nor is it more difficult to discern that, in the appendages of the tail, the middle division appears again and the outer vanishes; while, on the other hand, in the foremost jaw, the so-called mandible, the inner division only is left; and, in the same way, the parts of the feelers and of the eyestalks can be identified with those of the legs and jaws.

But whither does all this tend? To the very remarkable conclusion that a unity of plan, of the same kind as that discoverable in the tail or abdomen of the lobster, pervades the whole organisation of its skeleton, so that I can return to the diagram representing any one of the rings of the tail, which I drew upon the board, and by adding a third division to each appendage, I can use it as a sort of scheme or plan of any ring of the body. I can give names to all the parts of that figure, and then if I take any segment of the body of the lobster, I can point out to you exactly what modification the general plan has undergone in that particular segment; what part has remained movable, and what has become fixed to another; what has been excessively developed and metamorphosed and what has been suppressed. . . .

10

on the formation of specific anti-bodies in the blood following upon treatment with the sera of different animals, together with their use in legal medicine

G. H. F. NUTTALL and E. M. DINKELSPIEL

. . . Through the work of many investigators the complicated subject of immunity is gradually being solved, and we are beginning to understand the way in which the body combats or is protected against the inroads of disease. We have learnt of the existence of specific antitoxic, agglutinative, haemolytic, bactericidal and cellulicidal properties in the blood serum, etc., as also of a number of neutralizing bodies to these. The quite recent discovery of specific precipitins, which act upon various bacterial products, milks, peptone, egg albumin, and upon human blood and its derivates, has opened a wide field for investigation, which cannot fail to ultimately yield results of the greatest importance. . . .

The existence of specific precipitins in the blood was first demonstrated by Kraus who added cholera, plague, and typhoid anti-sera to filtrates of the cultures of the corresponding germs . . . .

In the following experiments only rabbits were used for obtaining the specific anti-sera. The blood, pleuritic exudation, etc., was injected intraperitoneally in quantities of 5 and 10 c.c., usually beginning with the smaller dose, the amount of 10 c.c. not being surpassed. Only a few injections were made subcutaneously, intraperitoneal injection being preferred. . . . The animals were regularly weighed every day, or every second day, and the injections were not repeated until they had regained any lost weight. The loss in weight was generally small and usually less after the first two injections. . . .

Reprinted with the permission of the Cambridge University Press from the Journal of Hygiene, Vol. 1 (1901), pp. 367-387.

Effective anti-sera were obtained after the fifth or sixth injection, sometimes earlier, as will be seen from the protocols. The animals were periodically bled by puncturing the lateral ear vein, the skin having been shaved, disinfected with lysol, and dried with sterilized cotton. The blood, as it flowed from the vein, was collected in fine-pointed sterilized bulbed pipettes from which it was expelled into test tubes which were laid almost horizontally into racks. . . .

In the following protocols the weights of the animals are given thus, "2500–2490 g.," this signifying that the weight at the beginning of the experiment was 2500 g., and at the conclusion 2490 g. The test for specific precipitins was made by adding about 3 drops of the treated animal's serum to a clear filtered 1:100 dilution of the blood, etc. with which it had been treated. Fluid serum was diluted with normal salt solution. Dried serum was dissolved in ten parts of normal salt-solution and this diluted 1:100. Dry blood was dissolved by means of water, as recommended by Uhlenhuth, to which an equal quantity of double NaCl solution (1.6%) was subsequently added. The results of the tests are given in the following protocols of our experiments. Where much precipitin was formed we refer to the reaction as "marked," etc. The test tubes used contained about 0.5 c.c. of blood dilution. When test serum flowed to the bottom of the tube the reaction was most striking at the line of contact between the fluids.

I. *Rabbits treated with Dog Serum.*

I. Weight 2460–2410 g. Treatment lasted 51 days. Received 6 injections, the first of 5 c.c. subcutaneously, the rest of 10 c.c. intraperitoneally, the last injection being made one week before the animal was bled to death from the carotids.

Bled 20 c.c. from ear after injection 3. *Marked reaction.*
Bled 20 c.c. from ear after injection 5. *Marked reaction. . . .*

II. *Rabbits treated with Sheep Serum and Defibrinated Blood.*

I. Weight 2270–2030 g. Under treatment 66 days. Received 7 intraperitoneal injections, the first of 5 c.c. defibrinated blood, the second of 5 c.c. fluid serum, the third of 7 c.c. normal solution of dried serum, the rest of 10 c.c. filtered serum.

Bled 25 c.c. from ear after injection 4. *Very slight reaction.*
Bled 4 c.c. from ear after injection 7. *Marked reaction. . . .*

VI. *Rabbits treated with Human Blood and Pleuritic Exudation.*

I. Weight 3070–2930 g. Under treatment 46 days. Received 6 intraperitoneal injections, each of 10 c.c. With the exception of injection 5, which was made with fresh serum, the animal only received pleuritic exudation which had been preserved for 5 to 6 months by the addition of chloroform, having been kept in a corked bottle at room temperature.

Bled 30 c.c. from ear after injection 4. *Reaction slight.*
Bled 40 c.c. from ear after injection 5. *Marked reaction.* . . .

The protocols of our experiments show that we obtained precipitins in the blood of rabbits treated with dog, sheep, ox, horse, and human blood. Our results have been negative in rabbits treated with the blood of the cat. The analogous observations of Bordet and Nolf have already been referred to.

The rest of the animals yielded an anti-serum which produced a marked reaction (much precipitum) after the third injection, in some the reaction only took place after the fifth injection. This does not seem to depend upon differences in the weights of the animals in relation to the dose of serum, but upon individual differences in the reacting power of the rabbits.

We have tested 36 kinds of blood up to the present, the bloods used being those of man, four species of monkey: *Cercopithecus campbelli* Waterh., *Cercopithecus patas,* W. coast of Africa, *Cercopithecus lalandii* Is. Geoffr. [S. Africa], *Macacus rhesus* [India], the Rufous Rat-Kangaroo (*Hypsiprymnus rufescens* [Gray], N. S. Wales), the Capybara (*Hyrochoerus capybara,* S. Tmerica), the polecat (*Mustela putorius*), Suricate (*Suricata tetradacyla* [S. Africa]), squirrel (*Sciurus vulgaris*), guinea-pig, tame and wild rabbit (*Lepus cuniculus*), white rat, black rat (*Mus rattus*), horse, ox, sheep, white-tailed gnu (*Connochaetes gnu,* S. Africa), gazelle (*Gazella arabica*), deer (*Cervus axis* Erxl.; India), dog, cat, pig, bat (*Plecotus auritus*), pigeon, chicken, pheasant, swan (*Cygnus olor*), duck, chaffinch (*Fringilla coelebs*), cross-bill (*Nucifraga caryocatactes*), rook *(Corvus fragilegus),* swallow (*Hirundo urbica*), corn-crake (*Crex pratensis*), frog (*Rana temporaria*), newt (*Molge cristata*), snake (*Tropidonotus natrix*).

The serum of rabbits treated with *dog serum,* added to all these bloods, gave a negative reaction throughout, excepting in the case of the dog. The tested dog blood was dried and dissolved in salt solution, or used in the form of diluted fluid serum. Whereas a marked and almost immediate precipitation occurred on the addition of the specific anti-serum to dog's blood, all the other blood solutions remained perfectly clear. . . .

The serum of the rabbits treated with *human* blood, serum, and pleuritic exudation only produced a marked precipitation in human blood solutions, etc. The blood of the four monkeys gave a slight but distinct reaction. A very faint clouding appeared in the solutions of the bloods of the horse, ox and sheep, whereas all the other bloods remained perfectly clear. The test gave positive results when made with diluted human serum, pleuritic exudation, both fresh and putrid, blood and serum which had been dried on filter paper and on glass plates, with blood which had undergone putrefaction for two months, with the blood of several persons who had cut themselves (blood collected on filter paper), with the serum from a blister on the foot following upon a long walk, and with the serum from a blister following a burn on the hand. Both nasal and lachrymal secretion gave a slight but decided reaction. A faint clouding was produced in normal urine. That the precipitum formed in putrid blood dilution was specific was proved by adding the anti-sera of rabbits treated with ox, sheep and dog serum to the blood dilution, no reaction resulting.

11

the mechanism of pancreatic secretion

W. M. BAYLISS and E. H. STARLING

. . . Our exact knowledge of many of the factors determining pancreatic secretion we owe to the work of Pavlov and his pupils, who have shown that the flow of pancreatic juice begins with the entry of the chyme into the duodenum and is not excited directly by the presence of food in the stomach itself. The exciting influence of the chyme is due chiefly to its acidity, and a large secretion can be brought about by the introduction of 0.4% hydrochloric acid into the stomach, whence it is rapidly transferred to the duodenum. Pavlov found, however, that other substances, *e.g.* water, oil, introduced into the stomach had a similar, though less pronounced, effect. . . .

Pavlov regards the secretion evoked by the presence of acid in the duodenum as reflex in origin, and ascribes the varying composition of the juice in different diets to a marvellous sensibility of the duodenal mucous membrane, so that different constituents of the chyme excite different nerve-endings, or produce correspondingly different kinds of nerve-impulses, which travel to the gland, or its nerve-centres, and determine the varying activity of the gland-cells. . . .

The question as to the mechanism by which a pancreatic secretion is evoked by the introduction of acid into the duodenum has been narrowed still further by the independent researches of Popielski and of Wertheimer and Lepage. These observers have shown that the introduction of acid into the duodenum still excites pancreatic secretion after

Reprinted with the publisher's permission from the Jounral of Physiology, Vol. 28 (1902), pp. 325-353.

section of both vagi and splanchnic nerves, or destruction of the spinal cord, or even after complete extirpation of the solar plexus. Popielski concludes, therefore, that the secretion is due to a peripheral reflex action, the centres of which are situated in the scattered ganglia found throughout the pancreas, and ascribes special importance to a large collection of ganglion cells in the head of the pancreas close to the pylorus. Wertheimer and Lepage, while accepting Popielski's explanation of the secretion excited from the duodenum, found that secretion could also be induced by injection of acid into the lower portion of the small intestine, the effect, however, gradually diminishing as the injection was made nearer the lower end of the small intestine, so that no effect at all was produced from the lower two feet or so of the ileum. Secretion could be excited from a loop of jejunum entirely isolated from the duodenum. They conclude that, in this latter case, the reflex centres are situated in the ganglia of the solar plexus, but they did not perform the obvious control experiment of injecting acid into an isolated loop of jejunum after extirpation of these ganglia. . . .

The apparent local character of this reaction interested us to make further experiments on the subject, in the idea that we might have here to do with an extension of the local reflexes whose action on the movements of the intestines we have already investigated. We soon found, however, that we were dealing with an entirely different order of phenomena, and that the secretion of the pancreas is normally called into play not by nervous channels at all, but by a chemical substance which is formed in the mucous membrane of the upper parts of the small intestine under the influence of acid, and is carried thence by the bloodstream to the gland-cells of the pancreas. . . .

III. The Effect of the Injection of Acid Into the Duodenum and Jejunum.

It is unnecessary to describe at length the results obtained under this heading. We are able to confirm the statements made by our predecessors. The result of injecting from 30 to 50 c.c. of 0.4% hydrochloric acid into the lumen of the duodenum or jejunum is to produce, after a latent period of about two minutes, a marked flow of pancreatic juice. Further, this effect is still produced after section of both vagi, section of the spinal cord at the level of the foramen magnum, destruction of the spinal cord, section of the splanchnic nerves, or extirpation of the solar plexus, or any combination of these operations. . . .

Our experiments, therefore, confirm those of previous observers in so far as we find that after exclusion of all nerve-centres, except those in the pancreas itself, a secretion of pancreatic juice is obtained by the introduction of acid into the duodenum. But, as pointed out above, the *experimentum crucis* of taking an isolated loop of intestine, dividing the mesenteric nerves supplying it, and then injecting acid into it, had not been performed. . . .

IV. The Crucial Experiment.

On January 16th, 1902, a bitch of about 6 kilos weight, which had been fed about 18 hours previously, was given a hypodermic injection of morphia some 3 hours before the experiment, and during the experiment itself received A.C.E. in addition. The nervous masses around the superior mesenteric artery and cœliac axis were completely removed and both vagi cut. A loop of jejunum was tied at both ends and the mesenteric nerves supplying it were carefully dissected out and divided, so that the piece of intestine was connected to the body of the animal merely by its arteries and veins. A cannula was inserted in the large pancreatic duct and the drops of secretion recorded. The blood-pressure in the carotid was also recorded in the usual way. The animal was in the warm saline bath and under artificial respiration.

The introduction of 20 c.c. of 0.4% HCl into the duodenum produced a well-marked secretion of 1 drop every 20 secs. lasting for some 6 minutes; this result merely confirms previous work.

But, and this is the important point of the experiment, and the turning-point of the whole research, the introduction of 10 c.c. of the same acid into the enervated loop of jejunum produced a similar and equally well-marked effect.

Now, since this part of the intestine was completely cut off from nervous connection with the pancreas, the conclusion was inevitable that the effect was produced by some chemical substance finding its way into the veins of the loop of jejunum in question and being carried in the blood-stream to the pancreatic cells. Wertheimer and Lepage have shown, however, that acid introduced into the circulation has no effect on the pancreatic secretion, so that the body of which we were in search could not be the acid itself. But there is, between the lumen of the gut and the absorbent vessels, a layer of epithelium, whose cells are as we know endowed with numerous important functions. It seemed therefore possible that the action of acid on these cells would produce a body capable of exciting the pancreas to activity. The next step in our experiment was plain, viz. to cut out the loop of jejunum, scrape off the mucous membrane, rub it up with sand and 0.4% HCl in a mortar, filter through cotton-wool to get rid of lumps and sand, and inject the extract into a vein. . . . The first effect is a considerable fall of blood-pressure, due, as we shall show later, to a body distinct from that acting on the pancreas, and, after a latent period of about 70 secs. a flow of pancreatic juice at more than twice the rate produced at the beginning of the experiment by introduction of acid into the duodenum. We have already suggested the name "secretin" for this body, and as it has been accepted and made use of by subsequent workers it is as well to adhere to it.

In the same experiment we were able to make two further steps in the elucidation of the subject. In the first place the acid extract was boiled and found undiminished in activity, secretin is therefore not of the nature of an enzyme. In the second place, since Wertheimer and Lepage have shown that the effect of acid in the small intestine diminishes in proportion as the place where it is introduced approaches the lower end, so that from the last 6 inches or so of the ileum no secretion of the pancreas is excited, it was of interest to see whether the distribution of the substance from which secretin is split by acids is similar in extent. Fig. 3 shows the result of injecting an extract from the lower 6 inches of the ileum made in the same way as the jejunum extract. The fall of blood-pressure is present, but there is no effect on the pancreas. Another preparation from the ileum just above this one also had no effect on the pancreas. A preparation from the jejunum below the previous one had a marked effect, but less than that of the loop above. The distribution of "prosecretin," as we have proposed to call the mother-substance, corresponds therefore precisely with the region from which acid introduced into the lumen excites secretion from the pancreas. . . .

12

on the transmission of the phototropic stimulus in the oat seedling

P. BOYSEN-JENSEN

In order to find out whether the phototropic stimulus in the oat coleoptile is transmitted in the vascular strands or in the parenchymatous tissue, Rothert dissected with a sharp knife both vascular bundles which are present in the coleoptile. It became apparent that the conduction of stimuli was not affected by this dissection. When he illuminated the tip on one side, a positive phototropic curvature appeared in the darkened basal part. Rothert concludes from his experiments: "It has thus been proven, that the heliotropic stimulus is transmitted in the parenchyma."

Later, Fitting studied this problem very thoroughly. Like Rothert, he too found that the conduction of stimuli is not arrested by a cross dissection, no matter how it is oriented in relation to the direction of light, whether the incision is on the front or back side, or on the flanks of the oat coleoptile. Fitting concludes that the polarity which is induced in all cells of the organ of perception by outer stimulus, progresses on living channels into the reaction zone, which is physiologically radially symmetrical and laterally apolar, so that all parts are "polarized" in this zone as well as in the cells of the channel for the conduction of stimuli.

Some experiments which I made in the Institute of Plant Physiology in Copenhagen before the publication of Fitting's work demonstrated a differing result. These experiments were then continued in the Institute of Plant Physiology in Leipzig in 1909.

Reprinted with the publisher's permission and that of Johnson Reprint Corporation from the Berichte d. Deutsche Botanische Gesellschaft, Vol. 28 (1910), pp. 118-120. Translated by Cynthia Faulhaber, 1965.

I discovered that when the incision was on the front side of the coleoptile (in relation to the direction of light) I got a very definite curvature in the darkened basal area; however, when the incision was on the back side, I got none. These experiments were made in fairly dry room air.

When I made these same experiments under water, I found that the dryness was not the cause of this differing result. The result of the experiments was exactly the same as in dry room air.

Now I imitated completely as possible the experimental conditions of Fitting. The experiments were made under an inverted glass in moisture-saturated air, and, in fact, with the same result as in Fitting's experiments.

Therefore: if the seedling is in very moist air, a conduction of stimuli occurs no matter how the incision is oriented in relation to the direction of light; if, however, the experiments are made in dry air, or under water, a conduction of stimuli occurs only when the incision is on the front side of the coleoptile and not when it is on the back side.

The positive results which I always got when the incision lay to the front convinced me that neither the perception ability nor the conduction of simuli and action ability were impaired in my plants. I therefore received the impression that the stimulus could progress only on the back side of the coleoptile, and that under certain conditions, it could progress over a wound.

In accord with this, the conduction of stimuli, as Fitting showed, is inhibited by inserting a sheet of mica into the incision, but only when the incision lies to the back. If, however, the sheet of mica is replaced by a thin piece of Calamus, which has very large vessels and allows the entry of water and dissolved matter, a conduction of stimuli occurs, even if the incision is on the back side.

My assumption first became certain when I succeeded in cutting the point off completely, then replacing it and still getting a positive phototropic curvature in the darkened basal area by lighting up one side of the point. The operation is conducted in the following manner: you dissect the coleoptile about 1 cm. from the tip with two wedge-shaped cuts without harming the foliage leaf which is inside the coleoptile. Then you take the tip of the coleoptile off, move the tip of the foliage leaf to about 2mm. above the wound, put a small drop of gelatin solution on the tip of the shortened foliage leaf, and put the cusp of the coleoptile back into its original position. The tip of the coleoptile is bound to the basal area by a ring of cocoa butter.

A definite conduction of stimuli then occurs if you illuminate the tip on one side and a strong curvature appears in the darkened basal area.

From these experiments it appears that the conduction of the phototropic stimulus takes place only on the back side of the coleoptile and that the stimulus can progress over a wound. . . .

13

on the growth-accelerating substances in the coleoptile of Avena sativa

FRITZ W. WENT

Paal, on account of his experiments, has been the first to assume a regulation of the growth in the coleoptile of Avena. This regulation is seated in the tip and must be caused by the local formation of a substance which, partly by diffusion, moves in a basipetal direction. Arrived in the growing zone it there accelerates growth. This substance or (substances) I shall for the sake of brevity call growth regulators. Of late years the growth-accelerating effect, exerted by the tip on the base, has been confirmed by direct growth measurements. Paal also says: "phototropic perception is perhaps a growth regulation, influenced by light." His idea is that the growth regulators, which normally are continually being formed by the tip, are by illumination of the tip either prevented from being formed, or are photochemically destroyed, or perhaps have their motion impeded by illumination . . . .

Miss Seubert tried to . . . [isolate growth regulators] by mixing the expressed juice of coleoptiles, in which these regulators must be present, with agar. Little blocks of this jelly were placed on one side of decapitated coleoptiles and from the resulting curvature it might be concluded whether this expressed juice had an influence on growth. It was found, however, that the juice expressed from tiplets and that from coleoptile rings had the same effect and always caused a growth retardation. Hence nothing could be concluded as to a growth-accelerating action of the tip.

Reprinted with the author's and publisher's permission from the Proceedings of the Section on Sciences of the Koninklijke Akademie van Wetenschappen te Amsterdam, Vol. 30 (1927), pp. 10-19.

So I made a different attempt. Paal's experiments had proved that diffusion of a phototropic stimulus also takes place through gelatine. I therefore placed a number of tips of coleoptiles of Avena closely together with their cut faces on a thin layer of gelatine. After about an hour I took off the tips again and placed the gelatine, cut into small blocks, on one side of decapitated plants. Already one hour later these plants began to show a negative curvature which after 3 hours had become strongly negative, sometimes amounting to an angle of 40° with the vertical. Gelatine on which no tips had been put, when placed on one side, gave no or a very feeble positive curvature, while gelatine on which coleoptile rings, cut off just below the tip, had stood, also produced no perceptible curvature. It was evident that I had obtained the more or less hypothetical growth regulators. For the curvature produced by placing gelatine blocks on one side indicates the difference in growth rate on the two sides of the coleoptile. This difference is caused by the influence of the gelatine on the underlying half of the coleoptile. The more the growth of this half is accelerated the stronger the curvature will be. Already the first experiments showed that on this foundation a quantitive method could be worked out in which the angle of curvature is the measure for the quantity of growth regulators, diffusing from the tiplets into the gelatine. For, if the unilaterally placed blocks were from the same portion of gelatine, also the curvatures of the stumps, expressed as angles, were pretty much the same. Taking an average of the angles with six plantlets, the mean error was as a rule not larger than 20%, and sometimes much smaller. This is particular striking, as phototropical curvatures often diverge widely. Two conclusions may be drawn: 1. the effect of a certain quantity of growth regulators on different stumps is the same, and 2. the curvature of the stump is a means for quantitatively determining the amount of growth regulators. So my experiments fall into two groups.

In the first place I am studying the formation and change of the growth regulators by various external circumstances, the curvature of the stumps after one-sided application of the gelatine being used as the means of analysis, and secondly I am examining how the stump reacts on the presence of growth regulators under different conditions. . . .

I will deal now with the influence of external circumstances on the formation of the growth regulators in the tip. It has already been stated that the length of the plantlets has scarcely any influence on the quantity produced.

One of the principal questions that may be answered by the present method is: what influence has light on the formation of growth regulators? The result of the experiments on this point might have been foreseen after Van Dillewijn's latest publication. The growth retardation observed by him after illumination from three sides with 800 metre-candle-seconds and the growth acceleration stated after 80,000 m.c.s. could only be caused by a smaller and by a larger formation of growth regulators. Ramaer could prove this growth retardation and acceleration in a different way. And finally Sierp came to the same conclusion from his experiments. Because the growth regulators formed during the illumination want some time before they have been so far conveyed downwards that an increase or diminution can make itself felt in the gelatine, I waited 30–40 minutes after illumination before cutting the tips and then kept them 45 minutes on the gelatine . . . .

From these data it appears very clearly that during a time of 35 to 80 minutes less growth regulators diffuse from the tips (having a length of 1–1.5 mm.) into the gelatine after applying 1000 m.c.s., but more after 100,000 m.c.s.

It was now also possible to imitate phototropic curves. To do this I first placed, as in all former experiments, on one side of the stump gelatine treated with tips to which an illumination of e.g. 100,000 m.c.s. had been applied. Then on the other side a gelatine block was placed, on which tips had stood that had been illuminated with ten times less light. In this way a gelatine system was placed on the stump which, according to Blaauw's theory, as nearly as possible approached the unilaterally illuminated tip. The plantlets indeed bent themselves in perfect accordance with the figures obtained by Arisz. With a difference of 1000 versus 0 m.c.s. a positive curvature (in 7 out of 9 plants, 2 remained straight) occurred, reckoned towards the 1000 m.c.s. With 10,000 versus 1000 m.c.s. the curvature was negative. With 100,000 versus 10,000 m.c.s. I found a positive curvature again, i.e. towards the 100,000 m.c.s.

This method is an improvement on that of Boysen-Jensen and Nielsen who placed a tip on both sides of a stump and illuminated only one of them. Another advantage of the present method is that while the gelatine stands on the stumps, no fresh growth regulators are formed, which might spoil the result. Ramaer already showed in 1926 that Jensen and Nielsen's conclusions were wrong, especially because they did not take into account the quantity of light applied. I provided a few plants in the above-described manner with two small pieces of gelatine, on which tips had stood, that had been illuminated with the same quantities of light which Ramaer had used. The result was that with 0 versus 1000 m.c.s. a curvature towards 1000 m.c.s. was observed, while with 0 versus 100,000 m.c.s. the curvature was reversed and turned away from the 100,000 m.c.s. This is in complete agreement with Ramaer's results.

14

studies on the growth hormone of plants. III. the inhibiting action of the growth substance on bud development

KENNETH V. THIMANN and FOLKE SKOOG

It has long been known that when the growing point of a young dicotyledonous plant is removed, the axillary buds on the stem below it begin to develop. As long as the terminal bud is present, the development of the axillary buds is inhibited. A lateral bud may also be inhibited by the rapid growth of another lateral above it, as we have found in our experiments, or opposite it, as in those of Dostál. Furthermore, Snow has shown that the inhibition, in *Pisum,* is principally due to the young leaves in the developing bud. The evidence indicates that this inhibition is probably caused by a special substance. There was reason to believe that this inhibiting substance is of the same nature as the growth-promoting substance of *Avena* coleoptiles, and the experiments to be described here confirm this belief.

1. *Methods.*—Young plants of *Vicia faba,* 4 to 6 weeks old, grown in the light, were used. The lowest lateral buds of these plants grow with great regularity. The plants selected were of approximately equal height and with as nearly as possible equal numbers of buds and leaves. The growth substance used was obtained from the growth of *Rhizopus suinus* and had an activity of about 2.10^{-6} mg. per plant unit. The activity of this growth substance and of that obtained from the *Vicia* plants was tested on *Avena* coleoptiles under the standard conditions described by Went, using the definition of units as given by Dolk and Thimann.

Reprinted with the authors' and publisher's permission from the Proceedings of the National Academy of Sciences, Vol. 19 (1933), pp. 714-716.

2. *Production of Growth Substance by Vicia faba.*—It was first found that the terminal bud produces growth substance in rather large quantities. From terminal buds of young plants 12 cm. high, 30 to 40 plant units diffused out into agar blocks in an hour. From the buds of older plants the amount obtainable was less. The undeveloped lateral buds produce practically no growth substance. When, however, the plant is decapitated and the lateral buds are undergoing rapid development, each bud produces almost one-half as much growth substance as the terminal bud of an intact plant. Small amounts of growth substance are also produced by the leaves, less than one plant unit per hour being obtainable from the oldest leaves, and about 5 plant units per hour from the youngest leaves under the conditions of the experiment. It is therefore clear that growth substance production is associated with the actively developing parts of the plants, and that rather large quantities of the substance are regularly passing into the stem.

3. *Inhibition of Bud Development by Growth Substance.*—In order to make quantitative determinations of the effect of applying growth substance to the plant, it was necessary first to determine the time required for growth substance to enter the plant from an agar block. By plotting the amount of growth substance remaining in agar blocks after different periods of application to the stem, it was found that 6 hours were necessary for a complete transference of growth substance into the stem.

Agar blocks containing growth substance were therefore applied to the tops of decapitated plants every 6 hours. Intact plants, and also plants to which blocks of plain agar were being applied, were used as controls. Measurements of the length of the lateral buds, and also of the main stem, were made daily. When the amount of growth substance applied was of the same order as that diffusing from the terminal bud into agar (160 plant units every 6 hours), a slight but definite inhibition of the development of the lateral buds was observed. When, however, the amount of growth substance applied was larger than that diffusing from the terminal bud (1400–1700 plant units every 6 hours), the development of lateral buds was completely inhibited. Thus, in one experiment, the mean increase in length of the lateral buds in 8 days was 3.4 ± 0.5 mm. in intact plants, 16.0 ± 2.7 mm. in decapitated controls and 1.8 ± 0.6 mm. in plants to which 1670 units of growth substance had been applied. Several such experiments were carried out, each comprising thirty to forty buds, and the amount of inhibition was similar in each case. The inhibition also takes place in the dark.

The necessity for applying larger amounts of growth substance than can be obtained from the terminal bud is fully justified on the ground that the application is generalized over the whole stem surface, while the normal supply from the tip is localized in the conducting tissue and therefore more effective in its action. Furthermore, there is evidence that wound substances may inactivate a part of the applied growth substance.

The inhibition is not to be ascribed to any damage, since the plants remained in good condition throughout the experiment, as was shown by the rapid development of the lateral buds as soon as the application of growth substance was stopped. While it is possible that the inhibition is due, not to the growth substance, but to another compound of similar nature present in the active concentrates, the present experiments make it probable that it is the growth substance itself, produced in the terminal bud, which inhibits lateral bud development.

Although it seems paradoxical that a substance promoting cell extension can also act as an inhibitor, this fact provides an explanation for much of the earlier work on inhibition, such as the experiments of Dostál, Snow and Weiskopf. The probable mechanism of the effect, together with a more detailed account of these experiments, will be published elsewhere.

15

the physiology of ecdysis in Rhodnius prolixus (Hemiptera). II. factors controlling moulting and 'metamorphosis'

V. B. WIGGLESWORTH

THE EFFECT OF DECAPITATION ON MOULTING

Moulting in Rhodnius occurs at a definite interval after feeding, only one meal being necessary in each stage. The fifth nymph, at 24° C., requires on an average about 28 days between feeding and moulting; the fourth nymph requires about 15 days; the earlier nymphs rather less. Insects at all stages have been decapitated at different times after feeding, and the effect on development observed. The head was removed by drawing a thread tightly round the neck in the larger insects; it was cut off with scissors in the smaller insects, the wound in each case being sealed with paraffin wax melting at 52° C.

The results . . . [show] that in each stage (as Kopeč found in the pupation of Lymantria) there is a critical period before which the head is necessary for moulting to occur. After this period moulting is no longer prevented by decapitation. In the fifth nymph the critical period occurs between the sixth and eighth days after feeding; in the earlier nymphs, from the third to the fifth day.

These headless insects digest their meal and excrete normally. Where they fail to moult they survive for long periods – several fifth nymphs survived more than 200 days, and one survived more than a year – far longer, indeed, than normal insects fed at the same time and kept under the same conditions. Where they moult, the process goes forward as already described. The insect usually dies when part way

Reprinted with the author's and publisher's permission from the Quarterly Journal of Microscopical Science, n.s. Vol. 77 (1933), pp. 191-222.

out of its old skin; in many cases the only sign that moulting is complete is the appearance of a film of air beneath the old cuticle – due to the absorption of the moulting fluid; but in one instance, that of a fourth nymph decapitated 4 days after feeding, the insect freed itself completely from the old skin . . . .

These results, coupled with the experimental effects of decapitation, suggest that the head is necessary for the production of a growth or moulting hormone; and that this hormone increases in amount until it reaches a critical concentration. At this stage (the critical period) mitoses in the epidermal cells begin, and thereafter the head is no longer needed.

THE STIMULUS TO MOULTING

The next question is the nature of the stimulus which brings about secretion of the moulting hormone. In the earlier paper it was shown that the time required for moulting is substantially the same whether the insect is fed a week after the previous moult or 9 weeks. The moulting cycle is clearly initiated by the new meal. Now if a succession of small meals is given at intervals, so that the stomach always contains a small amount of blood, moulting does not occur. (This was observed also by Kemper in the bedbug, Cimex.) It cannot therefore be the state of nutrition alone which determines moulting. It appears rather to be the abdominal distension.

This notion was tested experimentally as follows. After a meal of blood Rhodnius rapidly eliminates a large amount of fluid, quickly reducing the abdominal distension.

By occluding the anus with paraffin immediately after feeding, the distension for a given size of meal can be artificially exaggerated; and it is thus possible to study the effect of distension apart from that of nutrition . . . .

Normal fifth nymphs, which weigh from 30 to 50 mg. according to the time since they moulted, usually take a feed of between 200 and 300 mg. of rabbit blood. A meal as large as 420 mg. was noted in one instance. As shown . . . the smallest meal after which any normal nymph moulted was 98.6 mg.; the largest meal which failed to cause moulting was 115 mg. When the anus was occluded immediately after feeding, the smallest meal to cause moulting was 74.8 mg., and the largest which failed to cause moulting was 96.7 mg.

Thus stretching of the abdomen, combined of course with adequate nutrition, is probably the requisite stimulus to moulting. We have seen that the presence of the head is necessary for moulting to occur. This suggests that stretching exerts its effect by way of the nervous system.

(Excessive stretching, produced by occluding the anus immediately after a large meal, caused great delay in moulting and in some cases has inhibited it altogether. Kemper observed that excessive feeding of Cimex delayed moulting. Perhaps that was the same phenomenon.) . . .

DEMONSTRATION OF A MOULTING HORMONE IN THE BLOOD

If this idea is correct, the blood from an insect that has just passed the critical period should induce moulting in an insect decapitated before that period. This has been tested by cutting through the prothorax of the two insects, one shortly after the critical period, the other 24 hours after feeding, and fastening them together with paraffin wax so that the blood can flow freely from one to the other. In the early experiments the mixing of the blood was ensured by gently squeezing the two insects alternately; but this proved unnecessary.

In the first experiment, six fifth nymphs decapitated 8 days after feeding were joined to six fifth nymphs decapitated 1 day after feeding. Two of the former moulted, and both induced moulting in their partners. This experiment has been repeated many times with nymphs at different stages, and in every case where the insect decapitated soon after the critical period has moulted, it has induced moulting in its partner decapitated 24 hours after feeding . . . .

Now if the living nymphs are examined with a dissecting microscope while the epidermal cells are becoming separated and the new cuticle is being laid down, the body surface can be seen to go through a definite sequence of changes; and by observing these changes the stage of development can be approximately gauged. If daily observations are made on two insects that have been joined together, the onset of moulting is seen to be accelerated in the second insect (so that it may reach in 6 days a stage normally reached in 9 or 10 days), while the progress of moulting in the first insect appears to be delayed. This delay seems to last until the second insect has caught up the first; thereafter they develop together.

Thus it appears that not only is moulting initiated by a hormone, but the entire process is regulated, and parallel development in all parts of the body is ensured, by chemical substances in the blood. It is inconceivable that a single external factor should secure this exact co-ordination. These observations can only mean that the growing tissues themselves are communicating with and controlling one another by chemical means. This is a fundamental idea but it is beyond the scope of the present work, which is concerned only with the external or overriding factors which provide the initial stimuli to growth.

16

release of acetylcholine at voluntary motor nerve endings

H. H. DALE, W. FELDBERG and M. VOGT

In a note published some time ago, two of us gave a preliminary description of experiments which indicated that something having the properties of acetylcholine (ACh.) is liberated, when impulses in motor nerve fibres excite contraction of a voluntary, striated muscle. . . .

Our object has been to discover whether stimulation of the motor nerve fibres innervating voluntary muscle fibres, to the complete exclusion of the autonomic or sensory fibres running with them in a mixed nerve, causes the liberation of acetylcholine in appreciable quantities; and, if so, to endeavour to obtain evidence as to the site of such liberation . . . .

Most of our experiments have been made on the muscles of cats and dogs. These mammalian muscles are usually regarded as completely insensitive to the action of acetylcholine when their motor nerve supply is intact. Recent evidence, to be discussed later, shows that they are not, in fact, indifferent to acetylcholine in relatively large doses, applied through the circulation or directly; but their response, under such conditions, is by twitches or fibrillation, and they do not exhibit the slow contracture with which many muscles of the frog and other lower vertebrates respond to acetylcholine in low dilutions. It was accordingly of special importance to discover whether acetylcholine was liberated when motor impulses, causing only quick contractions, passed down the motor nerve fibres to such normal, mammalian muscles. A few experiments

Reprinted with the authors' and publisher's permission from the Journal of Physiology, Vol. 86 (1936), pp. 353-380.

were also made on frog's muscles, with stimulation of motor fibres separately from the other components of the mixed nerve . . . .

We have seen that, when stimulation of the motor fibres failed to produce contractions of the muscle, acetylcholine was no longer liberated. It was possible, therefore, that it might come from the muscle fibres themselves, as a by-product of the contractile process. It was further possible that fliud collecting in inadequately perfused areas, or in the tissue between the muscle fibres, might acquire acetylcholine from some source, and that contractions might mechanically press some of it into the perfusion stream. To test these possibilities we first studied the effects of producing contractions of the muscle by direct stimulation. A normally innervated muscle cannot be effectively stimulated without stimulating, at the same time, the branches and endings of motor nerve fibres in its substance. We accordingly made comparative experiments on normal muscles, and on corresponding muscles denervated by degeneration. The muscles chosen were again the gastrocnemius of the cat and the dog and the quadriceps extensor femoris of the dog, the sciatic or crural nerve on one side having been divided aseptically under ether 10 days previously.

The results with direct stimulation of the normally innervated muscles were not different from those produced by stimulating a similar muscle through its motor nerve supply. The first samples of venous effluent contained some acetylcholine, which disappeared with further perfusion. Stimulation of the muscle then caused acetylcholine to appear, as with motor nerve stimulation, and it disappeared as usual with further perfusion. With the denervated muscle the results were entirely different. In the first place, even the earliest samples of venous fluid, after it had become free from blood, showed no significant activity on the most sensitive leech preparation. Further, though the muscle contracted powerfully in response to direct stimulation, no trace of activity was shown by the fluid collected during or after the stimulation period . . . .

An experiment on a dog's quadriceps, deprived of its sympathetic supply by degeneration but otherwise normally innervated, showed that it gave the usual yield of acetylcholine to direct stimulation. Another experiment on a sympathetically denervated quadriceps gave a result of special interest. This muscle had initially responded normally by contractions, with output of acetylcholine, to motor nerve stimulation. With continued perfusion successive periods of such stimulation had been progressively less effective, till finally the muscle no longer contracted or yielded acetylcholine, with renewed stimulation of the nerve. Direct stimulation being now applied, the muscle contracted vigorously, but no trace of acetylcholine appeared in the venous fluid. The mechanism concerned with transmission of the excitatory process from the nerve to the muscle fibres being exhausted, acetylcholine was no longer liberated, though the muscle contracted well. The muscle, in this respect, behaved now like one which had been denervated . . .

The transmission of the effects of nerve impulses by a chemical substance, reaching the effector cells by diffusion, is now an accepted fact in the case of simpler types of contractile cells and tissues, usually displaying an automatic activity which the nerve impulses may modify in either direction. Such transmission by a diffusible stimulant can now be traced in the nervous control of most involuntary muscle, including, as we have seen, some which is striated and relatively quick in contraction. The question which here concerns us is whether in voluntary striated muscle, specialized for the quick contraction of individual fibres in response to nerve impulses, and normally at rest in their absence, this more primitive, chemical method of transmission has been superseded by an entirely different one, in which the chemico-physical disturbance constituting the nerve impulse passes, by continuous propagation, on to the muscle fibre; or whether, on the other hand, the required specialization has been effected by concentrating the release and the action of the chemical stimulant at the point of immediate contact of the nerve ending with the muscle fibre. . . . In the ganglion acetylcholine has been shown to be liberated in a concentration which effectively stimulates ganglion cells; while in the muscle we have shown that, when the liberation of acetylcholine fails by exhaustion, the excitation of the muscle no longer occurs. There seem to be two possibilities.

(1) That the propagated disturbance in the nerve fibre is directly transmitted to the effector cell, but that the latter cannot accept it for further propagation unless sensitized by the action of the acetylcholine, which appears with its arrival at the nerve ending. Such an hypothesis might be stated in terms of Lapicque's well-known conception, by supposing that the action of acetylcholine shortens the chronaxie of the nerve cell, or of the motor end plate of the muscle fibre, so that it is momentarily attuned to that of the nerve. H. Fredericq has observed, indeed, a shortening of the chronaxie of heart muscle by acetylcholine.

(2) That the acetylcholine, in these as in other cases, acts as the direct stimulant of nerve cell or muscle end plate, releasing an essentially new propagated wave of excitation in postganglionic nerve or muscle fibre, which, however, may so resemble that in the preganglionic or motor nerve fibre as to simulate an unbroken propagation. On this view there is no introduction of a new form of transmission, in evolution from the slowest and most primitive to the most rapid and special-

ized. The required rapidity of transmission is attained by concentrating the release of the chemical transmitter on the actual surface of the responsive structure.

Of the two possibilities, the latter appears to us to be more easily reconciled with the facts yet available concerning transmission at ganglionic synapses. The former would provide an explanation, alternative to that which we have considered earlier, for the apparently low sensitiveness of some normal muscles to stimulation by acetylcholine. The shortness of the delay in transmission appears to cause no greater difficulty for one conception than the other. The action of curare is explicable, in either case, as rendering the receptive element resistant to the action of acetylcholine, whether this be merely to sensitize or directly to stimulate. On the existing evidence we favour the second conception, while admitting that further facts are required for the exclusion or the establishment of either.

17

the general adaptation syndrome

HANS SELYE

Since the first description of the "alarm reaction" a decade ago, many publications have dealt with this phenomenon and with the "general adaptation syndrome," of which it forms a part. It is becoming increasingly more obvious that certain physiologic mechanisms, in which the endocrine system plays a prominent part, help to raise resistance to damage as such, irrespective of the specific nature of the damaging agents. Interest in the general adaptation syndrome has recently received a further impetus as a result of investigations suggesting that some of the most important diseases of human pathology (such as hypertension, nephrosclerosis and the rheumatic diseases) may represent by-products of the endocrine reactions, which are at play in the general adaptation syndrome. It was considered a timely enterprise, therefore, to survey this field now and to supply a guide to the rather scattered and polyglot, pertinent literature . . . .

Before entering upon a discussion of a relatively new concept, such as that of the general adaptation syndrome, it is essential to give a clear definition of the subject and the terminology to be used. In some sciences (*e.g.*, mathematics) definitions are unchangeable laws which make a concept what it is; in biology, however, definitions are given merely as concise descriptions of phenomena as they are known at the time, with the view of modifying them as soon as further observations necessitate it. It is with this in mind that the following definitions are presented.

Reprinted with the author's and publisher's permission from the Journal of Clinical Endocrinology, Vol. 6 (1946), pp. 117-230.

The general adaptation syndrome is the sum of all non-specific, systemic reactions of the body which ensue upon long-continued exposure to stress. It is distinct from the specific adaptive reactions, such as the development of the musculature following prolonged physical exercise, the allergic and immunologic phenomena elicited by foreign proteins or microorganisms, etc. These latter reactions usually endow the body with a great deal of resistance against the particular agent to which it has previously been exposed, but both the manifestations of these adaptive reactions and the resistance which they confer upon the body are specific to the agent which elicited them. . . .

It has been found, furthermore, that if an organism is continuously exposed to a certain type of stress, the resulting general adaptation syndrome evolves in three distinct stages, namely, those of the "alarm reaction," the "stage of resistance" and the "stage of exhaustion." Perhaps because historically the alarm reaction was the first to be described, or because of its striking name, it received the greatest attention in the literature. Indeed, some workers fail to distinguish clearly between the alarm reaction and the general adaptation syndrome as a whole. It is especially important, therefore, to emphasize that the former is merely the first stage of the latter.

The alarm reaction is the sum of all non-specific systemic phenomena elicited by sudden exposure to stimuli to which the organism is quantitatively or qualitatively not adapted. Some of these phenomena are merely passive and represent signs of damage or "shock," others are signs of active defense against shock. In the case of moderately severe damage, from which recovery is possible, most of the signs of damage become evident before the signs of defense. Hence, the alarm reaction may in turn be subdivided into two more or less distinct phases: the phase of *shock* and the phase of *countershock.* If exposure to damage is not very sudden or if the damaging agent to which the organism is exposed is relatively mild, countershock phenomena may become evident without any preceding phase of actual "shock." Unfortunately, no satisfactory definition of shock has as yet been given. In most cases one or the other symptom of shock was singled out as its basic feature and the condition was then defined as one characterized by that symptom (*e.g.*, hypothermia, hypotension, hemoconcentration, capillary permeability, hypochloremia, acidosis, depression of the nervous system, *etc.*). Such definitions are not satisfactory because under certain conditions any one of the so-called "characteristic" symptoms may be in evidence although there is no shock and conversely shock may develop in the absence of one or the other of these symptoms.

It seems more appropriate, therefore, to say that shock is a condition of suddenly developing, intense, systemic (general) damage. This definition, though perhaps not very instructive, is necessarily correct, since it is merely a brief outline of the essential phenomena which induced physicians to coin the term "shock." This latter term always implies a suddenly developing condition, so that damage caused by chronic ailments cannot be thus described. It also implies that the damage is systemic (or general) hence localized lesions, no matter how severe, should not be considered as shock unless they secondarily lead to generalized damage. . . .

The *stage of resistance* represents the sum of all non-specific systemic reactions elicited by prolonged exposure to stimuli to which the organism has acquired adaptation as a result of continuous exposure. It is characterized by an increased resistance to the particular agent to which the body is exposed and a decreased resistance to other types of stress. Thus the impression is gained that, during the stage of resistance, adaptation to one agent is acquired "at the expense of" resistance to other agents. It is also noteworthy that most morphologic and biochemical changes of the "alarm reaction" disappear during the stage of resistance and indeed in some cases the direction of the deviations from the normal is reversed (*e.g.*, hypochloremia during the alarm reaction, hyperchloremia during the stage of resistance).

Finally, *the stage of exhaustion* represents the sum of all non-specific systemic reactions which ultimately develop as the result of very prolonged exposure to stimuli to which adaptation had been developed, but could no longer be maintained. . . .

By *specific resistance* we mean that type of inurement which increases resistance only against the particular type of stress to which the body had been exposed; conversely, *non-specific resistance* designates the ability of the body to withstand stress qualitatively different from that to which it had been adapted.

The term "*adaptation energy*" is used to describe the ability of the organism to acquire resistance to stress. . . .

18

a relation between the effects of gibberellic acid and indolylacetic acid on plant cell extension

P. W. BRIAN and H. G. HEMMING

If gibberellic acid, a metabolic product of the fungus *Gibberella fujikuroi*, is applied to growing plants, it commonly causes a marked increase in stem internode length, mainly attributable to cell extension. Some dwarf varieties of pea are particularly sensitive, visible increases in internode-length resulting from doses of 0·01 μgm. gibberellic acid per plant. Auxins applied in a similar way have little or no effect; but, since auxins do induce cell extension in some circumstances, comparisons of the physiological effects of auxins and gibberellic acid have been made. It has been shown that gibberellic acid is inactive or of low activity in many conventional auxin assays, does not stimulate rooting of cuttings, does not inhibit development of lateral buds in decapitated plants, does not prevent leaf abscission and neither stimulates nor seriously inhibits root growth; similar observations have been made with the related material gibberellin *A*. Thus the spectrum of activity of gibberellic acid and gibberellin *A* is very different from that of the auxins; Kato has concluded that the mode of action is different from that of the auxins, but we have preferred to leave the question undecided in the absence of more positive evidence. We have recently made some observations which throw light on the relation of auxin activity to that of gibberellic acid.

We have used a technique adapted from Galston and Baker; 5-mm. sections, cut from unextended internodes of dwarf peas (var. Meteor)

Reprinted with the authors' and publisher's permission from Nature, Vol. 179 (1957), p. 417.

grown in light, are floated on phosphate buffer (*p*H 6·1), incubated at 15° C. in a light intensity of 800 ft.-candles, and the longitudinal extension of the sections measured after 24 hr. In a series of nineteen experiments with various concentrations of gibberellic acid in the buffer, only small increases in extension were produced, rarely reaching statistical significance; similar results were obtained when 2 per cent sucrose was added to the medium. Indolylacetic acid does induce extension of the sections, the optimal concentration being 10 μgm./ml. In the presence of such concentrations of indolylacetic acid, an extra effect is produced

TABLE 1

Mean length (mm.) of pea internode sections after 24 hr. growth in buffer with additions of sucrose, indolylacetic acid (10 μgm./ml.) and gibberellic acid (10 μgm./ml.); results of three experiments, all results being means of thirty replicates

Sucrose (per cent)	Other additions	I	II	III
None	None	6·8	6·8	6·6
	Indolylacetic acid	8·2	8·6	8·0
	Gibberellic acid	6·5	7·0	6·5
	Indolylacetic acid + gibberellic acid	9·0	9·1	8·3
2	None	6·9	7·6	6·6
	Indolylacetic acid	9·0	9·1	8·1
	Gibberellic acid	6·9	7·2	6·5
	Indolylacetic acid + gibberellic acid	9·6	9·9	10·0
Standard error		0·17	0·15	0·15

by gibberellic acid; the results of three experiments are summarized in Table 1. Factorial analysis of the data in each case showed a highly significant interaction between gibberellic acid and indolylacetic acid. Thus the former depends on the presence of the latter for its effect on cell elongation in the system studied, which would appear to approximate to conditions in the normal intact pea plant fairly closely. Furthermore, in so far as in the presence of optimal concentrations of indolylacetic acid still further growth is induced by gibberellic acid, it seems reasonable to conclude that its mode of action is different from that of indolylacetic acid, though in some way they are interdependent.

The concentration of gibberellic acid (10 μgm./ml.) used in the experiments just described is relatively high. In the presence of 10 μgm./ml. indolylacetic acid, a significant extension response is produced by 0·01 μgm./ml. gibberellic acid and a nearly maximum response by

0·1 μgm./ml. Even at 100 μgm./ml. gibberellic acid shows no toxic effects. Gibberellic acid significantly increases extension in the presence of indolylacetic acid in concentrations as low as 0·1 μgm./ml., but the greatest response is obtained in combination with 10 μgm./ml.

Though gibberellic acid alone does not significantly increase extension in light of internode sections from pea plants grown in light, it does induce elongation in darkness of sections from etiolated plants. This interesting difference is as yet unexplained.

19

movement of organic substances in trees

MARTIN H. ZIMMERMANN

How substances move in the phloem is one of the oldest of botanical questions. Trees are very suitable objects for studies of this movement because they offer the unique advantage of great lengths of uniform translocation conditions. However, working with trees has its difficulties. Large trees can hardly be grown under controlled conditions, and while most plant physiologists can transfer their material to a greenhouse or growth chamber, the tree physiologist has to take his experimental procedures to the trees outdoors. . . .

For physiological experimentation, trees, or parts thereof, are subjected to experimental conditions such as defoliation, girdling, and local chilling, and the effect of the treatment on translocation is studied. This can be done by paper-chromatographic analysis of sieve tube exudate from various parts of the tree and comparison of the results with those from normal trees. This procedure is based upon the assumption that what we call "sieve tube exudate" or "stylet exudate" is actually translocated material. Good evidence supports this assumption.

There are two methods for collecting sieve tube exudate. The "classical" method was the first described by Hartig in 1860. An incision is made into the inner bark, and the clear exudate can be collected with a graduated pipet. For quantitative studies, pipets of 5 cubic millimeters are most commonly used; occasionally pipets of smaller size are used, such as 2 or 4 cubic millimeters.

Reprinted with the author's and publisher's permission from Science, Vol. 133 (1961), pp. 73-79.

There are a number of organisms that have discovered the translocation channels as rich feeding grounds. . . . A most fascinating observation, made not long ago by entomologists, is that aphids do not suck but are being fed by the internal pressure of the sieve tubes: cut-off stylets from aphids which have been feeding continue to exude. This observation has been systematically developed into a method by Kennedy and Mittler, and by Mittler, with the willow aphid *Tuberolachnus salignus* (Gmelin). . . . Colonies of parthenogenetically reproducing females live on the lower side of branches during the summer. They insert their stylets into a sieve element of the conducting phloem. . . . When the stylet tips are properly placed in the phloem, as indicated by honeydew production, the insect can be cut from its mouth parts under anesthesia. If this is carefully done, exudation from the stylets continues, often for hours or even days, and the exudate can be collected with a pipet. . . .

THE MECHANISM OF TRANSLOCATION

The rate of phloem translocation is often extraordinarily high. According to Mason and Maskell it can be as much as 40,000 times the rate of sugar diffusion in water. The quest for the mechanism of this remarkable phenomenon has always greatly stimulated research. It appears to be clear that there are, in addition to rapid long-distance translocation in the phloem, other, usually much slower, types of transport in living tissues — movement in parenchyma cells, polar movement of auxins, secretion in nectaries.

Some workers regard long-distance movement in the phloem as a mass flow of solution; others visualize it as an active process involving translocation of solutes without solvent (water). Biddulph and Cory have recently even claimed two different transport mechanisms in the phloem, but their evidence is far from convincing. Whoever has been able to observe the rapid and consistent exudation from cut-off aphid stylets cannot doubt that we are dealing with a mass movement of a solution.

Theoretically, of course, stylet exudation per se is not proof of mass flow in the intact plant, because the stylets are artifacts. However, experimental work, by its very nature, involves artifacts, and all our knowledge about translocation is based upon indirect evidence. Rejection of the concept of mass flow raises the difficult question of how a single sieve element 20 to 30 microns in diameter and 0.4 millimeter long can be continuously refilled three to ten times per second with a concentrated sugar solution without any visible injury. . . .

The sieve tube vacuoles seem to represent a metabolic pool which is kept within by the semipermeability of the side-wall cytoplasm. The term *leaking* has often been used to describe how solutes get from sieve tubes to the surrounding tissue. This term is misleading. The sieve tubes do not leak. They remain turgescent for days and weeks after defoliation of a tree. Entry as well as exit of solute is a metabolic process that appears to be under remote control from the leaves. . . .

What is the mechanism of this solute entry into and exit from the sieve tubes? We know very little about it. Defoliation experiments suggest that we are dealing with enzymatic processes. As soon as the source of solutes – the leaves – is missing, we find a rapid increase of sucrose at the expense of oligosaccharides. An α-galactosidase, therefore, must be one of these removal enzymes. This enzyme is not in the sieve tube vacuole in solution; it is very probably attached to the sieve tube cytoplasm and is in contact with the vacuole. There are two reasons for this conclusion: (1) the enzyme does not appear in the exudate; (2) free galactose units do not appear in the exudate. Other enzymes, similarly placed, would be necessary to remove sucrose and mannitol (and all the other translocated substances) from the solution.

If we accept the idea that the sieve tube vacuole is a metabolic pool, we still have to explain how this pool is moving. Münch postulated in 1930 that differences in turgor pressure are sufficiently great to account for mass flow. His original hypothesis included all living cells of the plant. Later on his theory had to be restricted to the sieve tubes of the phloem because it was found that substances are often secreted into the sieve tubes against a concentration gradient. Within the sieve tubes, however, concentration gradients have always been found to be positive in the direction of flow. . . .

Studies of concentration gradients in trees in which several substances are being transported in major amounts are particularly interesting. In white ash the four substances stachyose, raffinose, sucrose, and mannitol make up the bulk of the exudate. During the summer one invariably finds that the total molar concentrations decrease in the downward direction of the trunk. After leaf abscission in autumn or after artificial defoliation at any time during the summer, the concentration of all substances drops, some of the individual gradients (often stachyose and mannitol) becoming negative and the others remaining positive. The result is the complete disappearance of the total molar gradient, indicating cessation of translocation.

The exudate concentration decreases some 0.01 mole per meter in the downward direction of a normal tree during the summer. According to Poiseulle's equation, the pressure gradient to which this would correspond is fully sufficient to force the solution through capillaries of the dimensions of the sieve tube lumen and the combined sieve pores at the observed rates. The difficulty is that the sieve pores are not open but are filled with cytoplasm. These so-called connecting strands often appear to be fairly dense in electron micrographs, but one should not forget that this density is considerably increased by growth of callose cylinders after wounding. Freezing the stem section on the intact plant (without wounding) is absolutely essential if connecting strands are to be studied by electron microscopy. The question of how much resistance the connecting strand represents cannot be answered at present, nor is there any way to calculate it. The suggestion has been made that electro-osmotic forces across the sieve plates may cause the solution to move. According to this theory the sieve plates would be not a passive resistance but the carrier of the electrical potential. Whatever may cause the solution to pass the sieve plates, we do know that it can pass easily. Mass flow of a solution is the only reasonable explanation for the refilling, three to ten times per second, of a sieve element with a highly concentrated sugar solution during hours and days of stylet exudation. . . .

Behavior

The way in which the intact organism responds to a given stimulus is referred to as behavior. Because plants are immobile, although not immotile, their behavior is restricted to relatively few, none the less fascinating, responses. For this reason, the study of stimulus-response is largely concerned with animal behavior. Certain facets of this field become indistinguishable from the province of the animal psychologist.

Observations on animal behavior appear in the literature of antiquity (see Aristotle, p. 196) and throughout much of the literature of biology, most notably in some of the writing of the great naturalists (p. 194). The systematic investigation of behavior, however, is first clearly indicated in a report by Spalding in 1872 (p. 68). By the turn of the current century, contemporary thinking became polarized into two camps, the trial and error "school" of which Jennings (p. 71) was pre-eminent, and the tropism (directed movement) "school" espoused by Jacques Loeb. Although these two opposing views are not exactly dead issues, they are no longer pre-emptory, at least in their original context.

Social organization, aggregational behavior, and the unifying factors in such organization has engaged the attention of a large number of biologists. Among the foremost students of social behavior in animals in the early decades of twentieth century biology in America was William Morton Wheeler (p. 79).

The physiological basis of behavior was extensively studied by Pavlov who is most widely recognized for his elucidation of the conditioned reflex (p. 75). It is of interest to note that Pavlov received the Nobel Prize in medicine in 1904 for his explanation of how digestion occurs.

Konrad Lorenz and Niko Tinbergen introduced a new era of conceptualization and analysis in behavior in the 1930s, a trend which, in the minds of many biologists, has led such studies out of the fold of animal behavior to animal psychology. Studies on communication among animals, using von Frisch (p. 83) as an example, suggest both the highly complex behavior of which so-called "simple" organisms are capable and the environmental parameters beyond the limited senses of man which are used both for communication and navigation.

The indistinct interdisciplinary boundary between psychology and biology, implicit in several of the preceding papers, has seen overt expresson in recent studies which have taken advantage of the high regenerative capacity of flatworms and the relative ease of their being conditioned. Further, there has been speculation that the RNA (ribosenucleic acid) molecule becomes modified in some way in the learning process. The paper by Corning and John (p. 86) has been included as representative of this as yet unconfirmed and controversial area of study.

20

instinct, with original observations on young animals

DOUGLAS A. SPALDING

Thus it would appear that with regard to instinct we have yet to ascertain the facts. With a view to this end, I have made many observations and experiments, mostly on chicken. The question of instinct, as opposed to acquisition, has been discussed chiefly in connection with the perceptions of distance and direction by the eye and the ear. Against the instinctive character of these perceptions it is argued that as distance means movement, locomotion, the very essence of the idea is such as cannot be taken in by the eye or ear; that what the varying sensations and feelings of sight and hearing correspond to must be got at by moving over the ground – by experience. On the other hand, it is alleged that though as regards man the prolonged helplessness of infancy stands in the way of the observer, we have only to look at the young of the lower animals to see that as a matter of fact they do not require to go through the process of learning the meaning of their sensations in relation to external things; that chickens, for example, run about, pick up crumbs, and follow the call of their mother *immediately* on leaving the shell. For putting this matter to the test of experiment, chickens, therefore, are most suitable and convenient subjects. I have observed and experimented on more than fifty chickens, taking them from under the hen while yet in the eggs. But of these, not one on emerging from the shell was in a condition to manifest an acquaintance with the qualities of the outer world. On leaving the shell they are wet and helpless; they

From Animal Behavior, Vol. 2 (1954), pp. 1-11, a reprint of the original article, with an introduction by J. B. S. Haldane, as it appeared in Macmillan's Magazine, Vol. 27 (1873), pp. 282-293.

struggle with their legs, wings, and necks, but are unable to stand or hold up their heads. Soon, however, they may be distinctly seen and felt pressing against and endeavouring to keep in contact with any warm object. They advance very rapidly. I have seen them hold up their heads well, peck at objects, and attempt to dress their wings when only between four and five hours old. But there is no difficulty in conceiving that with great spontaneity and a strong power of association much might be learned in four or five hours. Professor Bain is of opinion, from observations of his own on a newly dropped lamb, that "a power that the creature did not at all possess naturally got itself matured as an acquisition in a few hours." Accordingly, in the absence of precautions, the time that must elapse before chickens have acquired enough control over their muscles to enable them to give evidence as to their instinctive power of interpreting what they see and hear would suffice to let in the contention that the eye and the ear may have had opportunities of being educated. To obviate this objection with respect to the eye, I had recourse to the following expedient. Taking eggs just when the little prisoners had begun to break their way out, I removed a piece of the shell, and before they had opened their eyes drew over their heads little hoods, which, being furnished with an elastic thread at the lower end, fitted close round their necks. The material of these hoods was in some cases such as to keep the wearers in total darkness; in other instances it was semi-transparent. Some of them were close at the upper end; others had a small aperture bound with an elastic thread, which held tight round the base of the bill. In this state of blindness – the blindness was very manifest – I allowed them to remain from one to three days. The conditions under which these little victims of human curiosity were first permitted to see the light were then carefully prepared. Frequently the interesting little subject was unhooded on the centre of a table covered with a large sheet of white paper on which a few small insects, dead and alive, had been placed. From that instant every movement, with the date thereof as shown by the watch, was put on record. Never in the columns of a Court Journal were the doings of the most royal personage noted with such faithful accuracy. This experiment was performed on twenty separate chickens at different times, with the following results. Almost invariably they seemed a little stunned by the light, remained motionless for several minutes, and continued for some time less active than before they were unhooded. Their behaviour, however, was in every case conclusive against the theory that the perceptions of distance and direction by the eye are the result of experience, of associations formed in the history of each individual life. . . .

It would be out of place here to attempt to indicate the full psychological bearing of these facts. But this much may be affirmed, that they put out of court all those who are prepared only to argue against the instinctive perception by the eye of the primary qualities of the external world. When stripped of all superfluous learning, the argument against this and every other alleged case of instinctive knowledge is simply that it is unscientific to assume an instinct when it is possible that the knowledge in question may have been *acquired* in the ordinary way. But the experiments that have been recounted are evidence that prior to experience chickens behave as if they already possessed an acquaintance with the established order of nature. A hungry chick that never tasted food is able, on seeing a fly or a spider for the first time, to bring into action muscles that were never so exercised before, and to perform a series of delicately adjusted movements that end in the capture of the insect. This I assert as the result of careful observation and experiment; and it cannot be answered but by observation and experiment at least as extensive. It is no doubt common for scientific men to discredit new facts, for no other reason than that they do not fit with theories that have been raised on too narrow foundations. . . .

The only theory in explanation of the phenomena of instinct that has an air of science about it is Mr. Spencer's doctrine of Inherited Acquisition. The laws of association explain our intellectual operations and enable us to understand how all our knowledge may be derived from experience. A chicken comes on a bee, and, imagining it has found a dainty morsel, seizes the insect, but is stung and suffers badly. Henceforth bees are avoided; they can be neither seen nor heard without a shudder of fear. Now, if we can realize how such an association as this – how that one individual learns by experience may, in any degree, be transmitted to the progeny of that individual – we have a key to the mystery of instinct. Instinct in the present generation is the product of the accumulated experiences of past generations. The plausibility of this hypothesis, however, is not appreciated by the majority of even the educated portion of the community. But the reason is not far to seek. Educated men, even materialists – their own positive statements to the contrary notwithstanding – have not yet quite escaped from the habit of regarding mind as independent of bodily organization. Hence it is that while familiar with the idea of physical peculiarities passing by inheritance from one generation to another, they find it difficult to conceive how anything so impalpable as fear at the sight of a bee should be transmitted in the same way. Obviously, this difficulty is not consistent with a thorough belief in the intimate and invariable dependence of all kinds of mental facts on nervous organization. . . .

21

the method of trial and error in the behavior of lower organisms

HERBERT S. JENNINGS

. . . [Trial and error] has been found by Lloyd Morgan, Thorndike, and others to play a large part in the development of intelligence in higher animals. Intelligent action arises as follows: The animal works by the method of trial and error till it has come upon the proper method of performing an action. Thereafter it begins with the proper way, not performing the trials anew each time. Thus intelligent action has its basis in the method of "trial and error," but does not abide indefinitely in that method.

Behavior having the essential features of the method of "trial and error" is widespread among the lower and lowest organisms, though it does not pass in them so immediately to intelligent action. But like the dog bringing the stick through the fence the first time, they try all ways, till one shows itself practicable.

This is the general plan of behavior among the lowest organisms under the action of the stimuli which pour upon them from the surroundings. On receiving a stimulus that induces a motor reaction, they try going ahead in various directions. When the direction followed leads to a new stimulus, then try another, till one is found which does not lead to effective stimulation.

This method of trial and error is especially well developed in free-swimming single-cell organisms – the flagellate and ciliate infusoria – and in higher animals living under similar conditions, as in the Rotifera.

Reprinted from Contributions to the study of behavior in lower organisms. Carnegie Institution of Washington Publication 16 (1904).

In these creatures the structure and the method of locomotion and reaction are such as to seem cunningly devised for permitting behavior on the plan of trial and error in the simplest and yet most effective way.

These organisms, as they swim through the water, typically revolve on the long axis, and at the same time swerve toward one side, which is structurally marked. This side we will call *X*. Thus the path becomes a spiral. The organism is, therefore, even in its usual course, successively directed toward many different points in space. It has opportunity to try successively many directions though still progressing along a definite line which forms the axis of the spiral. At the same time the motion of the cilia by which it swims is pulling toward the head or mouth a little of the water from a slight distance in advance. The organism is, as it were, continually taking "samples" of the water in front of it. This is easily seen when a cloud of India ink is added to the water containing many such organisms.

At times the sample of water thus obtained is of such a nature as to act as a stimulus for a motor reaction. It is hotter or colder than usual, or contains some strong chemical in solution, perhaps. Thereupon the organism reacts in a very definite way. At first it usually stops or swims backward a short distance, then it swings its anterior end *farther than usual toward the same side X to which it is already swerving*. Thus its path is changed. After this it begins to swim forward again. The amount of backing and of swerving toward the side *X* is greater when the stimulus is more intense. . . .

But if we look closely at this simple method of reacting, we find it, after all, marvelously effective. The organism, as we have seen, is revolving on its long axis. When, as a consequence of stimulation, it swings its anterior end toward the side *X*, this movement is combined with the revolution on the long axis. As a consequence, the anterior end is swung about in a wide circle; the organism tries successively many widely differing directions. From each of these directions, as we have seen, a sample of water is brought to the sensitive anterior end or mouth. Thus the reaction in itself consists in trying the water in many different directions. As long as the water coming from these various directions evinces the qualities which caused the reaction – the greater heat or cold or the chemical – the reaction, with its swinging to one side, continues. When a direction is reached from which the water no longer shows these qualities, there is no further cause for reaction; the strong swerving toward the side *X* ceases, and the organism swims forward in the direction toward which it is now pointed. It has thus avoided the region where the conditions were such as to produce stimulation. . . .

In general terms we find that through this reaction by trial and error the organisms are kept in conditions favorable to their existence, and prevented from entering unfavorable regions. Through it they keep out of hot and cold regions and collect in regions of moderate temperature. Through it they tend to keep out of strong or injurious chemicals and out of regions where the osmotic pressure is much above or below that to which they are accustomed. Through it they gather in regions containing small amounts of certain chemicals, not leaving them for regions where there is either more or less of these chemicals. When oxygen is needed they collect through this reaction in regions containing oxygen; when the oxygen pressure is high, they do not react with reference to oxygen, or through this reaction they avoid regions containing much oxygen. Through this reaction organisms which contain chlorophyll, and therefore need light, gather in lighted regions or move toward the source of light; through the same reaction the same organisms avoid very powerful light. In all these cases, when there is error the organism goes back and tries a new direction, or a whole series of new directions.

This method of trial and error, which forms the most essential feature of the behavior of these lower organisms, is in complete contrast with the tropism schema, which has long been supposed to express the essential characteristics of their behavior. The tropism was conceived as a fixed way of acting, forced upon the organism by the direct action of external agents upon its motor organs. Each class of external agents had its corresponding tropism; under its action the organism performed certain forced movements, usually resulting in its taking up a rigid position with reference to the direction from which the stimulus came. Whether it then moved toward or away from the source of stimulus was determined by accidental conditions, and played no essential part in the reaction. There was no trial of the conditions; no indication of anything like what we call choice in the higher organisms; the behavior was stereotyped. Doubtless such methods of reaction do exist. In the reactions of infusoria to the electric current (an agent with which they never come into relation in nature), there are certain features which fit the tropism schema, and in the instincts – the "Triebe" – of animals there are features of this stereotyped character. The behavior of animals is woven of elements of the most diverse kind. But certainly in the lower organisms which we have taken chiefly into consideration the behavior is not typically of the stereotyped character expressed in the tropism schema. The method of trial and error is flexible; indeed, plasticity is its essential characteristic. Working in the lowest organisms with very simple factors, it is nevertheless capable of development; it leads upward.

The tropism leads nowhere; it is a fixed, final thing, like a crystal. The method of trial and error on the other hand has been called the "method of intelligence" (Lloyd Morgan); it involves in almost every movement an activity such as we call choice in higher organisms. With the acquirement of a *finer perception of differences* the organism acting on the method of trial and error rises at once to a higher grade in behavior. Combining this with the development of sense organs and the differentiation of motor apparatus, the path of advancement is wide open before it. . . .

22

physiology and psychology in the study of the higher nervous activity of animals

IVAN P. PAVLOV

. . . Several decades ago my laboratory made a study of digestion and investigated particularly the activity of the digestive glands and their elaborated juices by means of which the food is transformed so that it passes further into the depth of the organism and there enters into the vital chemical processes. Our problem was to study all the conditions under which the work of these glands was carried out. A large part of this investigation had to do with the first set of these glands, the salivary glands. The detailed systematic study of these organs showed that their work is extremely delicate, and very adaptable to whatever substance enters the mouth: the quantity of saliva and its quality vary in strict accordance to conditions. Dry food is taken, and much saliva flows, for the food must be moistened; with watery food, the amount of saliva is smaller. If there is food which must be passed into the stomach, the saliva secreted contains mucus, which lubricates the mass so that it is easily swallowed; if the substance is one which must be ejected, there is a thin, watery secretion to aid in rinsing the mouth. Here we see a number of delicate co-ordinations between the activity of these glands and the substance upon which the saliva is secreted.

Next rises the question, what is the basis of such a fine co-ordination, and what is its mechanism? For this the physiologist – and that is my specialty – has an answer ready. The properties of the food act on the

A lecture read before the Philosophical Society, Petrograd, November 24, 1916. Reprinted with the publisher's permission from Pavlov's Lectures on Conditioned Reflexes, translated by W. H. Gantt and G. Volborth. International Publishers Co., Inc., New York (1928).

nerve endings, stimulating them. These nervous impulses are conducted into the central nervous system to special points, and there cross over to the fibres leading to the salivary glands. Thus there is evidently a connection between what enters the mouth and the work of the glands. The details of this union are explained as follows: the several nerves from the oral cavity, where the substances act, are separately excited by acid, sweet, rough, soft, hard, hot, cold, etc., and these impulses travel along different nerve fibres to the central nervous system. From there these impulses can reach the salivary glands along different nerves. The one calls out one kind of activity; the others, other kinds. Consequently, different properties of the food stimulate separate nerves, and in the central nervous system there is a transfer to the corresponding nerves calling out each its particular function. . . .

We know very well that when we are hungry and want to eat, saliva flows if we see food. Hence the expression "the mouth waters." The investigation should extend to this phenomenon. What does it mean? There is, however, no kind of contact here. Concerning these facts, physiology used to say that besides the ordinary stimuli, there is a *psychical stimulation* of the salivary glands. Very well. But what does this mean, how is it to be understood, how must we physiologists approach it? Neglect it we cannot, once it plays a part in the action of the glands. What cause have we to exclude this function? First, let us consider the bare fact of psychical stimulation. It appears that psychical stimulation, *i.e.*, the action of a *substance at a distance, is absolutely the same as when it is in the mouth.* In every way it is the same. Judging by what kind of food is placed before the dog, if it is dry or moist, edible or inedible, the salivary glands function identically, whether the substance is in the mouth or at a distance. In the psychical stimulation we observe exactly the same relations, though the reaction is smaller. . . .

Now let us return to the work with which we are concerned. What, then, is the psychical stimulation of the salivary glands? When the food is placed in front of the animal, before his eyes, then it acts upon him, upon his eye, ear, nose. *There is here no essential difference from the action in the mouth.* They are reflexes from the eye and from the ear. When there is a loud sound, we reflexly jump. Stimulation with a strong light causes the pupils to contract. Consequently this (action from a distance) is no reason why we should not call the psychical stimulation a reflex. The *second element,* the nerve path: here the similarity is obvious; for when the dog sees the food the nervous path starts not in the mouth, but from the eye, continues to the central nervous system, and from here calls out the activity of the salivary glands. Again there is no real difference here and nothing prevents our representing this as a reflex. Now we come to the *third element,* its regularity. Regarding this it is necessary to say the following: The stimulation acts less regularly, less often on the salivary glands than when the substance is in the mouth. However, it is possible to study the subject and to handle it so that ultimately all those conditions upon which depends the action of the object at a distance will be under your control. Having attained to this point (and this is now the actual state of affairs), we are able to see regularity. But the psychical stimulation has an additional characteristic. When we examine these phenomena more closely it is seen that the agents acting from a distance are distinguished by this – that among them there can appear some which formerly were without effect. Here is an example. Let us say that the servant enters the room where the dog is and brings him food for the first time. The food began to act when the servant gave it to the dog. If the servant has brought the food for several days, then finally it is only necessary for the servant to open the door and put his head in, and the action begins at once. Here a new agent has appeared. If it continues thus long enough, then only the sound of the steps of the servant will be sufficient to evoke the saliva. In this way is created a stimulus which did not exist before. Evidently here is a considerable and important difference: in the physiological stimulation the stimuli are constant, but here they are changeable. . . .

It has been proved that *anything, whatever you will, from the external world can be made a stimulus of the salivary glands.* Any sound whatever, odour, etc. may become a stimulus, and it will call out the activity of the salivary glands as definitely as does food at a distance. In regard to the exactness of the fact, there is no difference whatever, only we must make allowance for the circumstances under which the fact exists. What then are these conditions under which anything can become a stimulus of the salivary glands? The basic prerequisite is *coincidence in time.* The experiment proceeds in this way: We take, for example, a sound, no matter what, which has no relation to the salivary glands. The sound acts on the dog, and he at the same time is fed, or acid is put into his mouth. After several repetitions of such a procedure the sound itself without either food or acid will stimulate the salivary glands. There are altogether four or five, perhaps six, conditions under which, in every dog, any stimulus, any agent of the external world inevitably becomes a stimulator of the salivary glands. Once this is so, once it has become such a stimulator under the definite series of circumstances, then it will always stimulate with the same accuracy as food or as some rejectable substance introduced into the mouth. If any agent of the external world inevitably becomes under certain circumstances a stimulator of the salivary glands, and having become such, inevitably acts, then what reason have we to say that this is anything other than a reflex? Here is a regular reaction of the organism to an external agent, brought about through the medium of a certain part of the nervous system. . . .

Thus, you see, that it is necessary to recognise the existence of two kinds of reflexes. One group of reflexes – ready from the time of birth – are purely conducting reflexes; but the other group – continually and without interruption being formed during the life of the individual, and just as regular as the first group – rest on the basis of another property of the nervous system, *viz.*, its ability to make connections. One reflex can be called inborn, the other acquired; the first generic, the second individual. The congenital, generic, constant, stereotyped one we term *unconditioned;* the other, because it depends upon a multitude of conditions and constantly fluctuates in correspondence with many circumstances, we called *conditioned,* showing in this way its characteristics as expressed from the point of view of the laboratory investigator. The conditioned reflex is also determined and therefore inevitable, and so it belongs, like the unconditioned reflex, entirely to the domain of physiology. By this formulation, physiology naturally comes into possession of an enormous mass of new material, because the number of these conditioned reflexes is legion. Life is made up of a mass of inborn reflexes. Obviously it is only an academic scheme to say that there are three kinds of reflexes – the self-preservative, the food, and the sexual. Their numbers are such that they must be divided and subdivided. Even of the congenital reflexes there are many, but the number of conditioned reflexes is infinite. Consequently, with the establishing of this new definition of conditioned reflexes, physiology lays claim to an enormous territory for investigation.

23

a study of some ant larvae with a consideration of the origin and meaning of the social habit among insects

WILLIAM MORTON WHEELER

The question arises as to whether there is any evidence that in other groups of social insects the salivary glands of the larva produce substances which are consumed by the worker nurses. Fortunately there are some very pertinent observations at hand in the French literature which is so rich in splendidly original works on the habits and taxonomy of insects. The observations to which I refer relate to the social wasps. Du Buysson observed that the larvae of *Vespa* "secrete from the mouth an abundant liquid. When they are touched the liquid is seen to trickle out. The queen, the workers and the males are very eager for this secretion. They know how to excite the offspring in such a way as to make them furnish the beverage." And Janet was able to prove that the secretion is a product of the salivary, or spinning, glands and that it flows from an opening at the base of the labium. "This product," he says, "is often imbibed by the imagines, especially by the just-emerged workers and by the males, which in order to obtain it, gently bite the head of the larva."

The most illuminating study of this matter, however, is found in a fine paper by Roubaud on the wasps of Africa. His account of the primitive wasps of the genus *Belonogaster* presents a striking picture of one of the earliest stages in the social life of wasps. . . .

Roubaud summarizes the general bearing of his observations in the following paragraph:

Reprinted with the publisher's permission from the Proceedings of the American Philosophical Society, Vol. 57 (1918), pp. 293-343.

The reciprocal exchange of nutriment between the adult females and the larvæ, the direct exploitation of the larval secretion without alimentary compensation by the males and just-emerged females are trophobiotic phenomena the elucidation of which is of great importance to an understanding of the origin of the social tendencies in the Vespidæ, as we shall show in the sequel. The retention of the young females in the nest, the associations between isolated females, and the cooperative rearing of a great number of larvæ are all rationally explained, in our opinion, by the attachment of the wasps to the larval secretion. The name *œcotrophobiosis* (from *oikos*, family) may be given to this peculiar family symbiosis which is characterized by reciprocal exchanges of nutriment between larvæ and parents and is the *raison d' être* of the colonies of the social wasps. The associations of the higher Vespids has, in our opinion, as its first cause the trophic exploitation of the larvæ by the adults. This is, however, merely a particular case of the *trophobiosis* of which the social insects, particularly the ants that cultivate aphids and coccids, furnish so many examples.

It does not seem to me that the term "œcotrophobiosis" is aptly chosen. Apart from its length, it implies, as Roubaud states, a relationship between adult and larval members of the same colony or family, comparable with that existing between ants on the one hand and aphids, coccids, membracids and lycænid larvæ on the other. This relationship, however, is, so far as nutrition is concerned, one-sided since the ants exploit the aphids, etc., and may defend or even transport them, but do not feed them. Moreover, even in *Belonogaster* the feeding of adults and larvæ is reciprocal, and the latter could not be reared if they were actually exploited to such an extent as to interfere with their growth. As the relationship is clearly cooperative or mutualistic, I suggest the term *trophallaxis* (from τροφή, nourishment and ἀλλάττειν, to exchange) as less awkward and more appropriate than "œcotrophobiosis." . . .

Although considerable evidence thus points to trophallaxis as the source of the social habit in wasps, ants and termites, it must be admitted that the phenomenon has not been observed in the social bees. That the latter may have passed through a phylogenetic stage like that of *Synagris* seems to be indicated by the solitary bees of the genus *Allodape* to which I have already referred. Brauns' observations, though meager, show nevertheless that *Allodape* has reached Roubaud's fourth stage, that of direct feeding of the larvæ from day to day, and if I am right in supposing that the peculiar appendages of the larvæ are exudate organs, there would be grounds for assuming that trophallaxis occurs in this case. On the other hand, it has often been suggested (*e.g.*, by von Buttel-Reepen) that the three social subfamilies, the stingless bees (Meliponinæ), bumblebees (Bombinæ) and honeybees (Apinæ) have developed from the solitary bees by another and more direct path, for the Meliponinæ, though living in populous societies, still bring up their brood in essentially the same way as the solitary bees, i.e., by sealing up the eggs in cells provisioned with honey-soaked pollen. The Bombinæ, however, keep opening the cells from time to time and giving the larvæ a little food at a time, and in the honeybee the cells are left open till pupation and the larvæ fed more continuously. Numerous facts indicate that the Bombinæ are the most primitive, the Apinæ the most specialized of existing social bees, and that the Meliponinæ, though closely resembling the solitary bees in the care of the young, are nevertheless in other respects very highly specialized (vestigial sting, elaborate nest architecture, etc.). It is therefore not improbable that these bees, after passing through a stage more like that of the Bombinæ, have reverted secondarily to a more ancient method of caring for their brood. . . .

Another objection that may be urged against the view that trophallaxis is so fundamental as I contend is the behavior of the ants towards their inert pupæ, which though transported and defended as assiduously as the larvæ yield neither liquid exudates nor secretions. This does not seem to me to be a serious objection, because the pupæ evidently have an attractive odor and may therefore be said to produce volatile exudates like certain myrmecophiles. Both the larvæ and pupæ, moreover, evidently represent so much potential or stored nutriment available for the adult ants when the food supply in the environment of the colony runs very low or ceases entirely. Infanticide and cannibalism then set in with the result that the devouring of the young of all stages may keep the adult personnel of the colony alive till the trophic conditions of the environment improve. Certain predatory tropical species (Dorylinæ, Cerapachyini) regularly raid the colonies of other ants and carry home and devour their brood. . . .

If we confine our attention largely to the ants, I believe it can be shown that trophallaxis, originally developed as a mutual trophic relation between the mother insect and her larval brood, has expanded with the growth of the colony like an ever-widening vortex till it involves, first, all the adults as well as the brood and therefore the entire colony; second, a great number of species of alien insects that have managed to get a foothold in the nest as scavengers, predators or parasites (symphily); third, alien social insects, *i.e.,* other species of ants (social parasitism); fourth, alien insects that live outside the nest and are "milked" by the ants (trophobiosis), and, fifth, certain plants which are visited or sometimes partly inhabited by the ants (phytophily). In other words the ants have drawn their living environment, so far as this was possible, into a trophic relationship, which, though imperfect or one-sided in the cases of trophobiosis and phytophily, has nevertheless some of the peculiarities of trophallaxis. . . .

24

the "language" and orientation of the bees

KARL von FRISCH

. . . A scout bee may find a good source of food near the home hive — it can be a flower with pollen or nectar or, in an experiment, a glass dish with sugar water. When the scout returns to the hive, she performs a round dance on the comb. This dance indicates symbolically to her hive mates that they should fly out and search around the hive. Inactive bees sitting near the dancer are thus aroused and stimulated to fly out. While they are still trooping after the dancer on the honeycomb, touching her with their antennae which bear the olfactory organs, they learn the kind of flowers for which they must search. Every species of flower has a specific odor. It clings to the scout bee which has collected from the flower, and it clings also to the nectar which she feeds the bees surrounding her during slight hesitations in her dance. The new collectors search for this odor and thus succeed in finding the correct goal. They too dance upon returning to the hive and after all subsequent collecting flights for as long as they find an abundant food supply. In this way the worker group becomes larger and larger as long as it is successful. . .

If the species of flower discovered in this way is more than 50 or 100 meters from the hive, then the round dance is supplanted by the "wagging" dance (Schwänzeltanz). The bee now moves in a straight line while wagging her abdomen vigorously; then she runs in a half-circle back to the starting point, and again the wagging course (Schwänzellauf), then a half-circle to the other side, and so forth. The wagging

Reprinted with the author's and publisher's permission from the Proceedings of the American Philosophical Society, Vol. 100 (1956), pp. 515-519.

dance means, like the round dance, that there is something to fetch outside. The flower species is identified by its odor, and the available yield through the spirit and duration of the dance. But in addition, this dance form conveys information about the distance to the goal and about the direction in which it lies.

The distance of the feeding area is shown by the rhythm of the dance. The more distant the food, the more slowly the turns of the dance follow one another; the fewer wagging courses occur therefore in a given time.

The direction of the Schwänzellauf conveys the direction of the goal, with reference to the position of the sun. This point is most clearly seen when the dance takes place on a horizontal surface and under a clear sky. One can observe it under these conditions if in warm weather part of the bee population loiters on the landing board just outside the hive entrance and some of the homecoming bees stop here to give up their load and to dance. They orient themselves in such a way that during the wagging course the sun is seen on the same side and at the same angle to their path as was the case on their flight to the feeding place. They thus point directly to the goal. The bees which troop after the dancing scout bees perceive this relationship relative to the sun, and since they assume this same position on flying out, they fly in the direction of the goal. . . .

To indicate direction in this way it is necessary to know the sun's position. What do the bees do when the sky is cloudy? The answer is as simple as it is surprising: they see the sun through a complete cloud cover. This can be demonstrated when one lays the observation hive on its side. On the horizontal surface the dancers orient their wagging course directly toward the goal. Under a cloudy sky they show the correct direction if they have a free view of that portion of the sky where, invisible to us, the sun stands behind the clouds, but their dances are completely disoriented if a board is interposed in the sun's direction and only cloudy sky is visible in other directions.

This perception of the sun through the clouds does not depend, as one might think, upon perception of infrared light, but rather on the sensitivity of the bees to ultraviolet light. Ultraviolet between 4,000 and 3,000 Å represents a distinct color for the bee's eye, and quantitatively their greatest visual sensitivity lies in this region. If under cloudy conditions, and with the hive horizontal, one places glass filters of selective spectral transmission above the dancers, one sees oriented dances only under those filters which transmit ultraviolet light in a particular range, and disoriented dances under filters which strongly filter out the ultraviolet. Whether, and to what degree, the visible and infrared light is transmitted has no bearing on the degree of orientation of the dances.

Should the sun stand behind a hill or be already set, the information system of the bees is undisturbed. But this is only the case if the sky is clear or at least a patch of blue sky is visible, for the blue light of the sky is to a large extent polarized, and its plane of polarization has a regular relationship to the position of the sun. Thus the bees have one more advantage over us in that they perceive the plane of polarization extremely well and can put it to use for their orientation. . . . The analyser for polarized light, to which they owe this ability, is located in the sensory cells of the compound eyes.

A problem seems to arise if the bees use the sun and the related polarized light pattern of the sky as a compass to inform their comrades of the direction of a goal. The magnetic compass always points to the north, but the sun is constantly changing its position. At first I thought that it would be useful only within short intervals of time, during which the sun's position would not shift significantly. An experiment has convinced me that I was wrong. Bees can also use the sky compass over long periods; they are capable of this because they possess a remarkable sense of time and because they are familiar with the daily path of the sun. One might say that they know just where it belongs at every hour of the day.

The experiment which led to this conclusion was the following: we transported a hive of bees to an unfamiliar region, opened the flight-hole in the afternoon and induced a group of marked bees to feed at a point 180 meters northwest of the hive during the afternoon and evening hours. The next morning the hive was again moved a great distance. The new surroundings were also unfamiliar and of a completely different character. The entrance to the hive was pointed in a new direction and then was opened as on the day before. Feeding tables were placed in four directions at the same distance, 180 meters. At each feeding place sat an observer who caught every bee as soon as it arrived so that she could not send others. In a short time the collecting bees from the day before appeared in overwhelming numbers at the northwest feeding dish; they therefore had searched in the training direction. Since they found no familiar landmarks in the unknown region, they could only have been guided by celestial navigation. And this occurred in the morning when the sun was in a completely different position from the direction in which the bees had seen it the previous afternoon and evening.

Numerous repetitions of these experiments and other types of observation besides prove that the bees can find one particular compass direction repeatedly whatever the time of day. Hence, the sun and the related polarized light pattern of the sky play an indispensable role for the bees, not only in the communication of direction, but in their general orientation as well. . . .

25

effect of ribonuclease on retention of conditioned response in regenerated planarians

W. C. CORNING and E. R. JOHN

Various data suggest that the neurophysiological mechanism of memory consists of two classes of process: (1) a short-term process, perhaps consisting of reverberatory electrical activity, and (2) a long-term process, by which neural excitability patterns are maintained by some sort of structural alteration. As radioisotope exchange data on brain compounds have accumulated, it has become apparent that these compounds seem to be characterized by rather rapid rates of turnover. In order to reconcile the persistence of memory with this lability of brain chemistry, it seems logical to search for a substance capable of maintaining a structural modification by imposing an experientially specified configuration on molecules being built in neural tissue. Imposition of the additional requirement that this substance be cytoplasmic in locus directs attention to ribonucleic acid (RNA). Essentially similar conclusions have been suggested in theoretical speculations by von Foerster and Hydén.

Some experimental data seem compatible with this suggestion. Brattgård has demonstrated a relationship between RNA synthesis and stimulation in retinal ganglion cells. Morrell has demonstrated histochemically an increase in RNA concentration which is a result of prior excitation. Kreps has reported differentially increased turnover of RNA in the cortical receiving area of the conditioned stimulus after elaboration of conditioned responses in the dog. In earlier work, John,

Reprinted with the authors' and publisher's permission from Science, Vol 134 (1961), pp. 1363-1365.

Wenzel and Tschirgi observed that injection of ribonuclease solution into the lateral ventricle of cats interfered with performance of pattern discrimination for food but not with a conditioned avoidance response to visual or auditory stimuli. The anatomical and chemical complexity of the preparation posed formidable obstacles to the gathering of control data necessary for unambiguous interpretation of these results. Rather than attempt to cope with these complexities, it seems desirable to devise a simpler preparation.

Recent reseach on the planarian has demonstrated that this comparatively simple organism is capable of learning both a classical conditioned response and a T-maze. Of particular relevance to our present concern was the finding that when cut in half and allowed to regenerate, both the head and tail sections display equal savings scores in both types of situations. Since there is cephalad dominance in these animals, the tail sections have in some manner apparently transmitted the effects of learning experience to the regenerated anterior portion. Experiments in our own laboratory, with the classical conditioned response, have confirmed the above findings. These various considerations suggested to us the possibility that RNA might play a role in the transmission of an acquired structural configuration from the trained portion to the regenerating tissue. Conditioned tails, regenerating in the presence of ribonuclease, might be expected to produce anterior portions with a depleted or altered RNA structure, perhaps due to influences exerted at the regenerating interface. Such an organism might then have a naive dominent head. Conversely, since trained heads have only a nondominant tail to regrow, they should demonstrate a greater degree of retention. Histological data provided by Chow indicate that planarian tails contain nerve somata, a fact clearly relevant to the aforementioned hypotheses.

In pilot work, we found that planarian tails could regenerate heads in pond water containing ribonuclease in concentrations of 0.1 mg/ml. The visible structural anomalies invariably obtained at this concentration indicated clear effects of the enzyme. In the experiments here reported, ribonuclease concentrations ranged from 0.07 to 0.1 mg/ml. Structural anomalies were seldom observed at the lower concentrations.

As reported elsewhere, paired presentation of light and shock to planarians results in the consistent appearance of a conditioned contraction and head movement to light alone. Specimens of *Dugesia dorotocephala* were divided into ten groups. In accordance with the design. . . base rates of response to light alone were determined. Worms were trained to the criterion of 34 conditioned responses per daily session of 40 trials; then they were transected into equal portions, which were allowed to regenerate for 14 to 18 days in either pond water alone or pond water containing ribonuclease. The regenerated portions were tested for 3 consecutive days for retention of the conditioned response to light alone, retrained to previous criterion, and then again tested for their response to light alone. . . .

The results . . . [show that] conditioned tails regenerated in ribonuclease do not retain the conditioned response. Conditioned heads similarly treated do not differ significantly from the controls. That ribonuclease does not affect intact tissue, as confirmed by results with groups IX and X, suggests that the effect occurs at the regenerating interface. Regeneration in ribonuclease does not interfere with acquisition as evidenced by groups III and IV. The configuration of the remaining control data permits us to rule out effects of transection alone, as well as temporal effects, in these results.

The savings scores obtained for retraining on groups I and II suggest that the tails treated with ribonuclease may retain some residual effects of the prior experience, although they are unable to transmit the effects to the regenerating tissue. A clearer understanding of these findings seems to require a more intimate understanding of the mechanism of information transfer, which we hope to obtain from electrophysiological and grafting experiments now in progress. While the results of this investigation do not establish the identity of the chemical substance responsible for the conditioned behavior of the regenerated animal, they appear entirely compatible with the assumption that this substance may be RNA. Further histological and biochemical explorations of this preparation are needed to evaluate this possibility adequately.

POPULATION LEVEL OF ORGANIZATION

The Nature and Interaction of Populations

At the population level of organization, the orientation is shifted to the groups of organisms sufficiently discrete from other groups as to be recognizable as a functional unity, a species. Isolated physiologically, morphologically and/or reproductively, if not geographically, such species populations have characteristics and attributes different from those of the discrete individuals comprising the group. Their characteristic features are also unique from those of others species populations.

Among the fundamental features of populations is the nature of their growth and regulation. The first clear statement on population growth and regulation occurred in the famous essay by Thomas Malthus in 1798 (p. 90), an essay whose influence, especially beyond the pale of biology, has been truly singular.

Populations, in general, are regulated by biotic and abiotic factors, by pressures external to the population and by forces within. Of the forces outside the population, the two major ones are competition and predation. Gause's excellent laboratory experiments on competition in the 1930s (p. 94) led to the well-known exclusion principle that two species cannot be sustained simultaneously if they have the same niche requirements. Using the field for his observations, one of the most noted of American conservationists, Aldo Leopold, detailed the effect of predators in population control (p. 98). A reconsideration from an ecological perspective of the role of several external forces in regulating population size and in determining community structure is developed in a fine example of sound logic by Hairston, Smith, and Slobodkin (p. 102). Finally, the study by Christian (p. 106) is included as an example of the role that internal factors may take in population regulation.

Population biology has a decidedly quantitative, paradigm-oriented thrust and has resulted in the development of a number of mathematical models of population growth and regulation. These aspects are slighted in the following selections, not as being inappropriate, but because they are, generally, too abstruse for the beginning student.

26

population: the first essay

THOMAS R. MALTHUS

It has been said that the great question is now at issue, whether man shall henceforth start forwards with accelerated velocity towards illimitable, and hitherto unconceived, improvement, or be condemned to a perpetual oscillation between happiness and misery, and after every effort remain still at an immeasurable distance from the wished-for goal. . . .

It is an acknowledged truth in philosophy that a just theory will always be confirmed by experiment. Yet so much friction and so many minute circumstances occur in practice, which it is next to impossible for the most enlarged and penetrating mind to foresee, that on few subjects can any theory be pronounced just that has not stood the test of experience. But an untried theory cannot fairly be advanced as probable, much less as just, till all the arguments against it have been maturely weighed and clearly and consistently refuted.

I have read some of the speculations on the perfectibility of man and of society with great pleasure. I have been warmed and delighted with the enchanting picture which they hold forth. I ardently wish for such happy improvements. But I see great, and, to my understanding, unconquerable difficulties in the way to them. These difficulties it is my present purpose to state, declaring, at the same time, that so far from exulting in them, as a cause of triumph over the friends of innovation, nothing would give me greater pleasure than to see them completely removed. . . .

Reprinted from chapter 1, first edition, Johnson, London (1798).

In entering upon the argument I must premise that I put out of the question, at present, all mere conjectures, that is, all suppositions, the probable realization of which cannot be inferred upon any just philosophical grounds. A writer may tell me that he thinks man will ultimately become an ostrich. I cannot properly contradict him. But before he can expect to bring any reasonable person over to his opinion, he ought to shew that the necks of mankind have been gradually elongating, that the lips have grown harder and more prominent, that the legs and feet are daily altering their shape, and that the hair is beginning to change into stubs of feathers. And till the probability of so wonderful a conversion can be shewn, it is surely lost time and lost eloquence to expatiate on the happiness of man in such a state; to describe his powers, both of running and flying, to paint him in a condition where all narrow luxuries would be condemned, where he would be employed only in collecting the necessaries of life, and where, consequently, each man's share of labour would be light, and his portion of leisure ample.

I think I may fairly make two postulata.

First, That food is necessary to the existence of man.

Secondly, That the passion between the sexes is necessary and will remain nearly in its present state.

These two laws, ever since we have had any knowledge of mankind, appear to have been fixed laws of our nature, and, as we have not hitherto seen any alteration in them, we have no right to conclude that they will ever cease to be what they now are, without an immediate act of power in that Being who first arranged the system of the universe, and for the advantage of his creatures, still executes, according to fixed laws, all its various operations.

I do not know that any writer has supposed that on this earth man will ultimately be able to live without food. But Mr. Godwin has conjectured that the passion between the sexes may in time be extinguished. As, however, he calls this part of his work a deviation into the land of conjecture, I will not dwell longer upon it at present than to say that the best arguments for the perfectibility of man are drawn from a contemplation of the great progress that he has already made from the savage state and the difficulty of saying where he is to stop. But towards the extinction of the passion between the sexes, no progress whatever has hitherto been made. It appears to exist in as much force at present as it did two thousand or four thousand years ago. There are individual exceptions now as there always have been. But, as these exceptions do not appear to increase in number, it would surely be a very unphilosophical mode of arguing to infer merely from the existence of an exception that the exception would, in time, become the rule, and the rule the exception.

Assuming, then, my postulata as granted, I say that the power of population is indefinitely greater than the power in the earth to produce subsistence for man.

Population, when unchecked, increases in a geometrical ratio. Subsistence increases only in an arithmetical ratio. A slight acquaintance with numbers will shew the immensity of the first power in comparison of the second.

By that law of our nature which makes food necessary to the life of man, the effects of these two unequal powers must be kept equal.

This implies a strong and constantly operating check on population from the difficulty of subsistence. This difficulty must fall somewhere and must necessarily be severely felt by a large portion of mankind.

Through the animal and vegetable kingdoms, nature has scattered the seeds of life abroad with the most profuse and liberal hand. She has been comparatively sparing in the room and the nourishment necessary to rear them. The germs of existence contained in this spot of earth, while ample food and ample room to expand in, would fill millions of worlds in the course of a few thousand years. Necessity, that imperious all-pervading law of nature, restrains them within the prescribed bounds. The race of plants and the race of animals shrink under this great restrictive law. And the race of man cannot, by any efforts of reason, escape from it. Among plants and animals its effects are waste of seed, sickness, and premature death; among mankind, misery and vice. The former, misery, is an absolutely necessary consequence of it. Vice is a highly probable consequence, and we therefore see it abundantly prevail, but it ought not, perhaps, to be called an absolutely necessary consequence. The ordeal of virtue is to resist all temptation to evil.

This natural inequality of the two powers of population and of production in the earth and that great law of our nature which must constantly keep their effects equal form the great difficulty that to me appears insurmountable in the way to the perfectibility of society. All other arguments are of slight and subordinate consideration in comparison of this. I see no way by which man can escape from the weight of this law which pervades all animated nature. No fancied equality, no agrarian regulations in their utmost extent could remove the pressure of it even for a single century. And it appears, therefore, to be decisive against the possible existence of a society, all the members of which should live in ease, happiness, and comparative leisure; and feel no anxiety about providing the means of subsistence for themselves and families.

Consequently, if the premises are just, the argument is conclusive against the perfectibility of the mass of mankind. . . .

27

competition for common food in protozoa

G. F. GAUSE

. . . At the beginning of the experiment into each tube were placed five *Paramecium*, or five *Stylonychia*, or five *Paramecium* plus five *Stylonychia* in the case of a mixed population. *Stylonychia* for inoculation must be taken from young cultures to avoid an inoculation of degenerating individuals.

(5) The growth curves of the number of individuals . . . are S-shaped and resemble our well-known yeast curves. After growth has ceased the level of the saturating population is maintained for a short time, and then begins the dying off of the population which is particularly distinct in *Stylonychia*. It is evident that this dying off is regulated by factors quite different from those which regulate growth, and that a new system of relations comes into play here. Therefore there is no reason to look for rational equations expressing both the growth and dying off of the populations. . . .

Stylonychia, and especially *Paramecium*, in a mixed culture attain lower levels than separately. The calculated coefficients of the struggle for existence have the following values: α (influence of *Stylonychia* on *Paramecium*) $= 5.5$ and β (influence of *Paramecium* on *Stylonychia*) $=$ 0.12. This means that *Stylonychia* influences *Paramecium* very strongly, and that every individual of the former occupies a place available for 5.5 *Paramecia*. With our technique of cultivation it is difficult to decide

Reprinted with the publisher's permission from The struggle for existence, Williams and Wilkins Co., 1934.

on what causes this depends. As a supposition only one can point to food consumption. . . .

(3) In an experiment of such a type all the properties of the medium are brought to a certain invariable "standard state" at the end of every 24 hours. Hence, we acquire the possibility of investigating the following problem: Can two species exist together for a long time in such a microcosm, or will one species be displaced by the other entirely? This question has already been investigated theoretically by Haldane, Volterra and Lotka. It appears that the properties of the corresponding equation of the struggle for existence are such that if one species has any advantage over the other it will inevitably drive it out completely. It must be noted here that it is very difficult to verify these conclusions under natural conditions. For example, in the case of competition between two species of crayfish a complete supplanting of one species by another actually takes place. However, there is in nature a great diversity of "niches" with different conditions, and in one niche the first competitor possessing advantages over the second will displace him, but in another niche with different conditions the advantages will belong to the second species which will completely displace the first. Therefore side by side in one community, but occupying somewhat different niches, two or more nearly related species . . . will continue to live in a certain state of equilibrium. There being but a single niche in the conditions of the experiment it is very easy to investigate the course of the displacement of one species by another. . . .

. . . The curves of growth of pure populations of *P. caudatum* and *P. aurelia* with different concentrations of the bacterial food show that the lack of food is actually a factor limiting growth in these experiments. With the double concentration of food the volumes of the populations of the separately growing species also increase about twice (from 64 up to 137 in *P. caudatum;* 64 × 2 = 128; from 105 up to 195 in *P. aurelia;* 105 × 2 = 210). Under these conditions the differences in the growth of populations of *P. aurelia* and *P. caudatum* are quite distinctly pronounced: the growth of the biomass of the former species proceeds with *greater rapidity,* and it accumulates a *greater biomass than P. caudatum at the expense of the same level of food resources.* . . .

(3) We will now pass on to the growth of a mixed population of *P. caudatum* and *P. aurelia*. . . . For a detailed acquaintance with the properties of a mixed population we will consider the growth with a half-loop concentration of bacteria. First of all we see that as in the case examined before the competition between our species can be divided into two separate stages: up to the fifth day there is a competition between the species for seizing the so far unutilized food energy; then

after the fifth day of growth begins the redistribution of the completely seized resources of energy between the two components, which leads to a complete displacement of one of them by another. The following simple calculations can convince one that on the fifth day all the energy is already seized upon. At the expense of a certain level of food resources which is a constant one in all "half-loop" experiments and may be taken as unity, *P. aurelia* growing separately produces a biomass equal to 105 volume units, and *P. caudatum* 64 such units. Therefore, one unit of volume of *P. caudatum* consumes $\frac{1}{64} = 0.01562$ of food, and one unit of volume of *P. aurelia* $\frac{1}{105} = 0.00952$. In other words, one unit of volume of *P. caudatum* consumes 1.64 times as much food as *P. aurelia,* and the food consumption of one unit of volume in the latter species constitutes but 0.61 of that of *P. caudatum.* These coefficients enable us to recalculate the volume of one species into an equivalent in respect to the food consumption volume of another species.

On the fifth day of growth of a mixed population the biomass of *P. caudatum* (in volume units) is equal to about 25, and of *P. aurelia* to about 65. If we calculate the total of these biomasses in equivalents of *P. aurelia,* we shall have: $(25 \times 1.64) + 65 = 106$ (maximal free growth of *P. aurelia* is equal to 105). The total of the biomasses expressed in equivalents of *P. caudatum* will be $(65 \times 0.61) + 25 = 65$ (with the free growth 64). This means that on the fifth day of growth of the mixed population the food resources of the microcosm are indeed completely taken hold of.

(4) The first period of competition up to the fifth day is not all so simple as we considered it in the theoretical discussion of the third chapter, or when examining the population of yeast cells. The nature of the influence of one species on the growth of another does not remain invariable in the course of the entire first stage of competition, and in its turn may be divided into two periods. At the very beginning *P. caudatum* grows even somewhat better in a mixed population than separately . . . apparently in connection with more nearly optimal relations between the density of Paramecia and that of the bacteria in accordance with the already mentioned data of Johnson. At the same time *P. aurelia* is but very slightly oppressed by *P. caudatum.* As the food resources are used up, the Johnson effect disappears, and the species begin to depress each other as a result of competition for common food.

It is easy to see that all this does not alter in the least the essence of the mathematical theory of the struggle for existence, but only introduces into it a certain natural complication: the coefficients of the struggle for existence, which characterize the influence of one species on the growth of another, do not remain constant but in their turn undergo regular alterations as the culture grows. . . .

28

deer irruptions

ALDO LEOPOLD

From the fifteenth century until 1910, the deer problem of North America was a matter of too few, rather than of too many.

About 1910 the Kaibab deer herd in Arizona, long stabilized at a level of about 4000 head, began to pyamid its numbers. By 1918 the range showed overbrowsing. Between 1918 and 1924, seven successive investigators warned of impending disaster, but nothing was done.

In 1924, at a probable level of 100,000 head, came the first of two catastrophic famines which reduced the herd 60 per cent in two winters. By 1939 the herd had dropped to a tenth of its peak size, and the range had lost much of its pre-irruption carrying capacity.

This was the first of a series of irruptions which have since threatened the future productivity of deer ranges from Oregon to North Carolina, California to Pennsylvania, Texas to Michigan. Wisconsin is one of the more recent irruptive states. . . .

(B) *Kaibab Plateau.* Unlike the George Reserve irruption, which was terminated by removing deer, the Kaibab irruption terminated itself by starvation. Some deer were in fact removed, but only after starvation had begun. The period of six years between the first warning (1918) and the final catastrophe (1924) was consumed in debate and litigation.

The effect of prolonged overstocking on the winter food plants was very severe. In 1931, after four-fifths of the herd had starved and only 20,000 deer were left, one investigator says "the range had been so

Reprinted with the publisher's permission from the Wisconsin Conservation Bulletin, Publication 321 (1943), pp. 1-11.

severely damaged that 20,000 was an excessive population. The herd continued to decrease slowly until an estimated 10,000 were present in 1939."

Another investigator estimates the loss in carrying capacity as high as 90 per cent in some areas.

In short, the Kaibab, by reason of the irruption, lost a large part of its deer food without any gain in deer. . . .

COMMON CHARACTERS

These histories exhibit certain common characters of deer herds, of deer food plants, and of human attitudes toward deer, which seem worth recording as background for the Wisconsin problem.

They also exhibit a common sequence of stages which may help to interpret current events, to anticipate research needs, and to guide administrative policy.

Winter Food. Deer irruptions are a problem in winter food. The summer range usually exceeds the winter range in carrying capacity.

Except in agricultural regions where deer have access to corn, alfalfa, or winter grains, deer subsist in winter mainly on twigs, buds, and catkins of woody plants, i.e. "browse." The browse species differ in palatability. Many investigators have shown that palatable browse is nutritious browse, while unpalatable browse cannot sustain deer in winter.

As a herd increases, the pressure on palatable browse plants weakens them and ultimately kills them. It also prevents their reproduction, or the emergence of their reproduction above snow level. Artificial plantings to reëstablish browse are eaten up before they have a chance to grow.

The unpalatable species are thus given a competitive advantage over palatable ones, and replace them. . . .

Winter Deer Behavior. Most animals, when crowded and hungry, disperse by their own social pressure. Deer herds, at least in winter, seem devoid of such pressure. State after state reports instances of deer stubbornly refusing to leave (or even to be driven from) a depleted winter range. Paraphrased in human terms, "deer would starve rather than move."

This trait results in *spotty* damage to the winter range. The Kaibab, Pennsylvania, New York, and Michigan, all report this spotty character, and it is now visible in Wisconsin. It confuses laymen, who see spots of undamaged winter browse and conclude that no crisis exists.

Perhaps wolves and cougars originally performed for deer the function of dispersal from congested spots which most species perform for themselves.

Limitations of Artificial Feeding. The first human reaction to deer starvation is always an impulse to feed the herd, rather than to reduce it. Winter feeding of game birds and songbirds carries no known penalties, why not feed the deer?

The main difference lies in the effect of artificial feeding on the supply of natural foods. . . .

Deer, on the other hand, subsist on palatable browse which is limited in quantity. Over-consumption progressively reduces next year's growth by attrition, nonreproduction, and replacement. Hence artificial deer food is not a net addition to natural food, and may become a net subtraction. For this reason, the most experienced states have come to doubt the wisdom of artificial feeding, except temporarily, or in emergency. . . .

PREDISPOSING EVENTS

Predators. We have found no record of a deer irruption in North America antedating the removal of deer predators. Those parts of the continent which still retain the native predators have reported no irruptions. This circumstantial evidence supports the surmise that removal of predators predisposes a deer herd to irruptive behavior.

In weighing this question, one must distinguish between the substantial removal of predators and the extirpation of the last individual. . . .

In most parts of the west, the substantial extirpation of deer predators took place within a decade after 1910, when the present system of paid hunters came into full-scale operation. Thus on the Kaibab, wolves were a factor in 1910 but gone by 1926. Cougars were abundant up to about 1915; they are still present but are now kept reduced to a very low level. The Kaibab deer irrupted almost immediately after the extirpation of wolves and the substantial removal of cougars. . . .

Coyotes do not seem to be effective predators in the sense of controlling irruptions, for the Kaibab herd irrupted in the presence of numerous coyotes. . . .

It appears, then, that cougars and wolves are the most effective deer predators. The evidence available supports the surmise that their removal does not cause irruptions, but paves the way for irruptive behavior, either at once or at some future time.

Cuttings. It is common knowledge that in humid regions, where the original forests were so dense as to shade out browse, deer "followed the slashings," i.e. did not become abundant until after large areas had been converted to brush. Thus there were few or no deer around Lake

Superior before the lumbering era, and deer have spread north into Canada coincident with cuttings. . . .

Buck Laws. Laws protecting antlerless deer predispose a herd to irruptive behavior to the extent that they are enforced, for the killing of males in a polygamous species has, within ordinary limits, no effect on reproductive rate. . . .

Fire. There is general agreement that a little fire improves deer range, but that wholesale burning destroys it. When deer happen to irrupt a decade or two after the first effective fire control, damage to deer and range is exaggerated by the closure of tree crowns, for this shades out much browse at a time of maximum need for browse. The present deer crisis in Wisconsin is exaggerated by the present closure of tree crowns which grew up following the fire-control system established about 1930.

In parts of the west, there was widespread reproduction of forest trees following early overgrazing and later fire control. These new forests have now closed their crowns, and thus shaded out much browse. . . .

29

community structure, population control, and competition

NELSON G. HAIRSTON, FREDERICK E. SMITH,
and LAWRENCE B. SLOBODKIN

The purpose of this note is to demonstrate a pattern of population control in many communities which derives easily from a series of general, widely accepted observations. The logic used is not easily refuted. Furthermore, the pattern reconciles conflicting interpretations by showing that populations in different trophic levels are expected to differ in their methods of control.

Our first observation is that the accumulation of fossil fuels occurs at a rate that is negligible when compared with the rate of energy fixation through photosynthesis in the biosphere. Apparent exceptions to this observation, such as bogs and ponds, are successional stages in which the failure of decomposition hastens the termination of the stage. The rate of accumulation when compared with that of photosynthesis has also been shown to be negligible over geologic time.

If virtually all of the energy fixed in photosynthesis does indeed flow through the biosphere, it must follow that all organisms taken together are limited by the amount of energy fixed. In particular, the decomposers as a group must be food-limited, since by definition they comprise the trophic level which degrades organic debris. There is no a priori reason why predators, behavior, physiological changes induced by high densities, etc. could not limit decomposer populations. In fact, some decomposer populations may be limited in such ways. If so, however, others must consume the "left-over" food, so that the group as a

Reprinted with the authors' and publisher's permission from The American Naturalist, Vol. 94 (1960), pp. 421-425.

whole remains food-limited; otherwise fossil fuel would accumulate rapidly.

Any population which is not resource-limited must, of course, be limited to a level *below* that set by its resources.

Our next three observations are interrelated. They apply primarily to terrestrial communities. The first of these is that cases of obvious depletion of green plants by herbivores are exceptions to the general picture, in which the plants are abundant and largely intact. Moreover, cases of obvious mass destruction by meteorological catastrophes are exceptional in most areas. Taken together, these two observations mean that producers are neither herbivore-limited nor catastrophe-limited, and must therefore be limited by their own exhaustion of a resource. In many areas, the limiting resource is obviously light, but in arid regions water may be the critical factor, and there are spectacular cases of limitation through the exhaustion of a critical mineral. The final observation in this group is that there are temporary exceptions to the general lack of depletion of green plants by herbivores. This occurs when herbivores are protected either by man or natural events, and it indicates that the herbivores are able to deplete the vegetation whenever they become numerous enough, as in the cases of the Kaibab deer herd, rodent plagues, and many insect outbreaks. It therefore follows that the usual condition is for populations of herbivores *not* to be limited by their food supply.

The vagaries of weather have been suggested as an adequate method of control for herbivore populations. The best factual clues related to this argument are to be found in the analysis of the exceptional cases where terrestrial herbivores have become numerous enough to deplete the vegetation. This often occurs with introduced rather than native species. It is most difficult to suppose that a species had been unable to adapt so as to escape control by the weather to which it was exposed, and at the same time by sheer chance to be able to escape this control from weather to which it had not been previously exposed. This assumption is especially difficult when mutual invasions by different herbivores between two countries may in both cases result in pests. . . .

The remaining general method of herbivore control is predation (in its broadest sense, including parasitism, etc.). It is important to note that this hypothesis is not denied by the presence of introduced pests, since it is necessary only to suppose that either their natural predators have been left behind, or that while the herbivore is able to exist in the new climate, its enemies are not. There are, furthermore, numerous examples of the direct effect of predator removal. The history of the Kaibab deer is the best-known example, although deer across the northern portions of the country are in repeated danger of winter starvation as a result of protection and predator removal. . . .

Thus, although rigorous proof that herbivores are generally controlled by predation is lacking, supporting evidence is available, and the alternate hypothesis of control by weather leads to false or untenable implications.

The foregoing conclusion has an important implication in the mechanism of control of the predator populations. The predators and parasites, in controlling the populations of herbivores, must thereby limit their own resources, and as a group they must be food-limited. Although the populations of some carnivores are obviously limited by territoriality, this kind of internal check cannot operate for all carnivores taken together. If it did, the herbivores would normally expand to the point of depletion of the vegetation, as they do in the absence of their normal predators and parasites.

There thus exists either direct proof or a great preponderance of factual evidence that in terrestrial communities decomposers, producers, and predators, as whole trophic levels, are resource-limited in the classical density-dependent fashion. Each of these three can and does expand toward the limit of the appropriate resource. We may now examine the reasons why this is a frequent situation in nature.

Whatever the resource for which a set of terrestrial plant species compete, the competition ultimately expresses itself as competition for space. A community in which this space is frequently emptied through depletion by herbivores would run the continual risk of replacement by another assemblage of species in which the herbivores are held down in numbers by predation below the level at which they damage the vegetation. That space once held by a group of terrestrial plant species is not readily given up is shown by the cases where relict stands exist under climates no longer suitable for their return following deliberate or accidental destruction. . . .

A second general conclusion follows from the resource limitation of the species of three trophic levels. This conclusion is that if more than one species exists in one of these levels, they may avoid competition only if each species is limited by factors completely unutilized by any of the other species. It is a fact, of course, that many species occupy each level in most communities. It is also a fact that they are not sufficiently segregated in their needs to escape competition. Although isolated cases of nonoverlap have been described, this has never been observed for an entire assemblage. Therefore, interspecific competition for resources exists among producers, among carnivores, and among decomposers.

It is satisfying to note the number of observations that fall into line with the foregoing deductions. Interspecific competition is a powerful selective force, and we should expect to find evidence of its operation. Moreover, the evidence should be most conclusive in trophic levels where it is necessarily present. Among decomposers we find the most obvious specific mechanisms for reducing populations of competitors. The abundance of antibiotic substances attests to the frequency with which these mechanisms have been developed in the trophic level in which interspecific competition is inevitable. The producer species are the next most likely to reveal evidence of competition, and here we find such phenomena as crowding, shading, and vegetational zonation.

Among the carnivores, however, obvious adaptations for interspecific competition are less common. Active competition in the form of mutual habitat-exclusion has been noted in the cases of flatworms and salamanders. The commonest situation takes the form of niche diversification as the result of interspecific competition. This has been noted in birds, salamanders, and other groups of carnivores. Quite likely, host specificity in parasites and parasitoid insects is at least partly due to the influence of interspecific competition.

Of equal significance is the frequent occurrence among herbivores of apparent exceptions to the influence of density-dependent factors. The grasshoppers described by Birch and the thrips described by Davidson and Andrewartha are well-known examples. Moreover, it is among herbivores that we find cited examples of coexistence without evidence of competition for resources, such as the leafhoppers reported by Ross and the psocids described by Broadhead. It should be pointed out that in these latter cases coexistence applies primarily to an identity of food and place, and other aspects of the niches of these organisms are not known to be identical. . . .

30

phenomena associated with population density

JOHN J. CHRISTIAN

. . . Some years ago we proposed that population growth and decline were regulated by series of feed-back mechanisms, particularly involving the pituitary-adrenocortical and pituitary-gonadal systems, and that these in turn were activated by socio-psychological factors (intraspecific competition) within the population. Present evidence indicates that interacting behavioral and endocrine mechanisms comprise at least an important part of such a system in the individuals in a population: a system responding to changes in the number of animals in such a way that population growth is self-limiting and self-regulating. This paper will summarize the evidence for such a mechanism. . . .

To show that the mechanism outlined above actually is effective in regulating population growth, one must demonstrate increased adrenocortical and decreased reproductive functions with increased size of a population. Experiments to explore these relationships were conducted in the laboratory with populations of fixed size, with freely growing populations of house mice and voles and, subsequently, with natural populations of a number of species in the field.

In the first series of experiments, male mice which had been caged singly at weaning were placed in groups of from 3 to 32 per cage with adequate numbers kept singly as controls. Food and water were supplied in excess of usage at all times. Organ weights were obtained after sacrifice a week later. The mean organ weight from all of the mice

Reprinted with the author's and publisher's permission from the Proceedings of the National Academy of Sciences, Vol. 47 (1961), pp. 428-449.

in a population (single cage) was used as the unit of measurement (one degree of freedom) in order to establish that the observed effects are due to changes in the population and not to so-called "within cage" effects, in these and, whenever possible, in all subsequent experiments to be described.

Adrenal weight, presumably a measure of adrenal function under the chronic conditions of these experiments, increased with increasing density of the population in both albino and wild-stock house mice. . . . Thymus weight, using involution of the thymus as an indicator of adreno-cortical function, decreased with increased density of population, especially in the wild-stock mice. The weights of the preputial glands, seminal vesicles, and testes declined progressively with increasing density, indicating inhibition of reproductive function at the gonadal as well as at the pituitary level. The decline in weights of the sex accessories presumably reflects a proportional decline in the secretion of testicular androgens. . . .

This experimental design was based on the assumption that the stimulus to increased adrenocortical and decreased gonadal function was socio-psychological or competitive in nature, acting through higher centers – the hypothalamus, the anterior pituitary, and thence to the pituitary target glands. Therefore, to check the effects of density *per se* and the possible role of increased exercise, experiments were run with populations of the same size as before, except that the cages had 42 times more area. . . . In spite of the greater space the adrenal responses were comparable to those in the preceding experiments, although the numbers of populations used were not adequate to determine quantitative relationships with the same degree of precision. Therefore within the spatial limits used the response of the mice was not to density *per se*, but rather to the presence of other mice.

The relationship between physiological response and social factors was further explored in experiments with wild-stock mice in which the responses of individual mice in each of a number of populations were investigated. Mice rank themselves much like chickens, in a series of dominance-subordinance relationships, and this characteristic was utilized in these experiments. Adrenal weight was least in the dominant animals and greatest in the most subordinate animals, while the mean adrenal weights of animals in the intermediate ranks were strung out in between these two extremes in a more or less linear fashion. . . . Finally, the impression was gained from observing grouped mice that the more clear-cut the rank differences are, the less the physiological response to "density" implying that populations in which rank differences are clearly established may reach a greater size than those in which rank differences are less well defined. . . .

Experiments to test the effects of injury and fighting show that the adrenal and reproductive responses to grouping occur with or without fighting and irrespective of the absence or, when present, of the degree of injury. However, probably the strongest argument against attributing these effects to fighting is the graded adrenal weight with social rank, with the dominant animal showing little increase in adrenal weight compared to the subordinate animals, whereas the dominant animals fight at least as much and probably more than the subordinate animals.

Competition for food or deprivation of food does not contribute to the observed changes in adrenal weight. In fact, the results of experiments suggest that these animals cannot anticipate a food shortage and, consequently, that each mouse in a population is equally affected by a restricted supply of food, irrespective of its rank. Food, whether abundant or scarce, scattered or localized, did not appear to affect competition and therefore had no effect on adrenal activity in house mice, either directly or indirectly. However, Frank presents evidence that a shortage of food may increase competition in voles (*Microtus arvalis*) and therefore may be effective in other species.

The experiments discussed so far were with males of house mice or other species, but earlier experiments had shown that reproduction by female mice declines with increasing population size, and that the dominant females in a group do most of the reproducing. Subsequently it was shown that maturation was inhibited in grouped, compared with isolated, female mice in the absence of males. . . .

Increased density affects reproductive performance and lactation of female mice. If females are kept in groups of 20 mice of each sex per cage for six weeks, and subsequently removed, and then each female placed in a cage with a previously isolated male, the reproductive function of the female is severely curtailed. The growth of the young is also inhibited, as compared to appropriate controls. Many never bear young, although nearly all become pregnant only to resorb the young early in pregnancy. Those that bear litters do so much later than controls placed with males at the same time, and the average number of ovulations and the mean litter size are less. The young nursed by these mice are stunted at the time of weaning due to deficient lactation and not to *in utero* effects, as shown by the normal growth of young born to previously crowded mothers which were removed and fostered by previously isolated females. Finally, these effects on the pups are lasting. When they are maintained as *isolated* pairs of one female and one male each, their offspring are in turn stunted at weaning, although the effect is observable only in litters of 8, 9, or 10 compared to 6 and above for the preceding generation. When these young are bred, in turn, their pups are stunted, but not significantly.Crowding clearly has a profound effect on every aspect of reproduction, with prolonged effects on the offspring. Similar results have been described from experiments with voles (*Microtus*).

One of the actions of the adrenal glucocorticoids is to decrease resistance to infection by inhibiting inflammation, granulation, phagocytosis, and antibody formation. These experiments demonstrate that increased density, presumably through inhibition of defense mechanisms by increased endogenous adrenal corticoids, can increase mortality by reducing resistance to infectious disease. These results explain why epidemics, paradoxically often involving a variety of pathogens, are frequently but not always seen in natural populations of mammals at peak numbers.

The foregoing experiments demonstrate the following basic effects of increases in population density: increased adrenocortical activity, depression of reproductive functions with increasing size of the population, inhibition of growth, inhibition of sexual maturation, decreased resistance to disease, and inhibition of growth of nursing young with effects on subsequent generations, apparently through deficient lactation. However, these experiments were highly artificial and the question remains whether similar effects can be observed in populations which have been permitted to grow of their own accord, either in the laboratory or in the field. . . .

The Categorizing of Populations

Man's seeming proneness to order, systematize, and classify sees expression in biology in an area referred to as taxonomy. Taxonomy, the classifying of organisms, actually has several implications. In the more restricted sense, it includes the naming of organisms by prescribed nomenclatural procedure and the providing of description sufficiently acute as to permit no doubt of distinction of one from another kind of organism. In a broader context, taxonomy is concerned with the ranking of organisms into hierarchies based on similarities and differences, largely morphological but not exclusively so. Both facets of taxonomy imply that there are valid criteria for recognition of both the species and its phylogenetic relationships.

The potential confusion in the naming of organisms has been circumvented largely by the simple (in retrospect) device of giving an organism two names, generic and specific. This ordering step is credited to Linnaeus in the mid-eighteenth century, but it is generally acknowledged that it originated in the work of John Ray and of Francis Willoughby. It was Linnaeus, however, who first consistently applied this binomial system (p. 112).

Initially and for more than one hundred fifty years following Lineaus, gross morphology constituted the major criterion for classification. The concern for valid criteria and for a natural system of taxonomy were focal points of a great deal of biology throughout the nineteenth century. Louis Agassiz's essay on classification in 1857 (p. 115) is representative of these discussions.

The twentieth century has witnessed a number of alternative approaches to systematizing groups of organisms. A biochemical basis was introduced indirectly by Nuttall's discovery of antibody production in the miscegenation of various sera (p. 32). It has found application in such studies as those by Bate-Smith on the use of phenolics in classification (p. 126). The introduction of statistical methods came in the studies by the nonbiologist, engineer Laurence Klauber on rattlesnakes in the

1930s (p. 118). Perhaps the most challenging affront to classical taxonomy has come in the critical studies of Clausen, Keck, and Hiesey in the 1930s and 1940s and their insistence on the need for an experimental approach to taxonomy (p. 122).

31

the families of plants

CARL von LINNAEUS

All the real knowledge, which we possess, depends on Method; by which we distinguish the similar from the dissimilar. The greater number of natural distinctions this method comprehends, the clearer becomes our idea of the things. The more numerous the objects, which employ our attention, the more difficult it becomes to form such a method; and the more necessary. The great Creator has in no part of his works presented a greater variety of objects to the human mind than in the vegetable kingdom; which covers the whole globe, which we inhabit; whence, if a distinct method is ever necessary, it is necessary here; if we hope to gain a distinct knowledge of vegetables. Thus Cesalpinus, "unless plants be reduced into orders, and like the squadrons of an army distributed into their proper classes, every thing must be in a state of fluctuation."

2. To him therefore vegetables are known, who (1) can join the similar to the similar, and can separate the dissimilar from the dissimilar.

3. The botanist is he, who can affix similar names (2) to similar vegetables, and different names to different ones, so as to be intelligible to every one.

4. The names (3) of plants are *generic*, and (where there are any species), *specific*. These should be certain and well founded, not vague, evasive, or variously applicable. Before they can be such, it is necessary

Reprinted from the preface of the English translation (translator unknown), John Jackson, Litchfield (1787).

that they should have been affix'd to certain, not to vague, genera. (2.6) for if this foundation be unsteady, the names also, and in consequence the doctrine of the botanist crumbles into ruin. (3)

5. The species are as numerous as the different and constant forms of vegetables, which exist upon this globe; which forms according to instinctive laws of generation produce others, similar to themselves, but in greater numbers. Hence there are as many species, as there are different forms or structures of plants now existing; excepting such less different *varieties*, which situation or accident has occasion'd.

6. The genera are as numerous, as the common proximate attributes of the different species, (5), as they were created in the beginning; this is confirm'd by revelation, discovery, observation, hence *the genera are all natural.*

For we must not join in the same genus the horse and the swine, tho' both species had been one-hoof'd, nor separate in different genera the goat, the raindeer, and the elk, tho' they differ in the form of their horns. We ought therefore by attentive and diligent observation to determine the limits of the genera, since they can not be determin'd a priori. This is the great work, the important labour, *for should the genera be confused, all would be confusion.*" Cesalpinus.

7. That it has pleased Infinite Wisdom to distinguish the genera of plants by their fructification was discover'd in the last age; and first indeed by Conradus Gesner, the ornament of his time; as appears from his posthumous epistles, and from the plates published by Camerarius, altho' the first, who introduced this great discovery into use, was Andreas Cesalpinus; which would nevertheless have shortly expired in its cradle, unless it had been recalled into life by the care of Robert Morison, and nourish'd by Joseph P. Tournefort with pure systematic rules. This was at length confirm'd by all the great men, then existing, in the science.

8. This foundation being given (7), this point fix'd, immediately every one capable of such researches join'd their labours to turn it into use, to build a system; all with the same inclination, and to the same purpose, but not all with equal success. . . .

. . . I wish it therefore to be acknowledged by all true botanists, if they ever expect any certainty in the science, that *the genera and species must be all natural;* without which assumed principle there can be nothing excellent done in the science. . . .

9. Having assumed this postulatum (8) every one proceeded according to his own method; they distributed these genera into orders and classes; Cesalpinus, Hermmannus, Ray, Knaut, according to the fruit; Tournefort from the *figure of the corol;* Rivinus from *the number*

and equality of the petals; Magnol from *the calyx,* all these methods have been attended with no injury to the science; . . .

10. These natural genera assumed, (6, 7) two things are required to preserve them pure, first that the true species, and no others, be reduced to their proper genera. Secondly that all the genera be circumscribed by true limits or boundaries, which we term *generic characters.*

11. These *characters,* (10) as I turn over the authors, I find uncertain and unfix'd before *Tournefort;* to him therefore we ought deservedly to ascribe the honor of this discovery of ascertaining the genera. . . .

12. *Tournefort* did wonders with his characters, but since so many and such new genera have been since discovered; it should be our business to adhere indeed to his principles, but to augment them with new discoveries, as the science increases.

13. *Figures* alone for determining the genera I do not recommend; before the use of letters was known to mankind, it was necessary to express everything by picture, where it could not be done by word of mouth, but on the discovery of letters the more easy and certain way of communicating ideas by writing succeeded. . . .

29. The use of some botanic system I need not recommend even to beginners, since without system there can be no certainty in botany. Let two enquirers, one a systematic, and the other an empiric enter a garden fill'd with exotic and unknown plants and at the same time furnish'd with the best botanic library; the former will easily reduce the plants by studying the letters (11) inscribed on the fructifications to their class, order, and genus; after which there remains but to distinguish a few species. The latter will be necessitated to turn over all the books, to read all the descriptions, to inspect all the figures with infinite labour; nor unless by accident can be certain of his plant. . . .

32

essay on classification

LOUIS AGASSIZ

Modern classifications of animals and plants are based upon the peculiarities of their structure; and this is generally considered as the most important, if not the only safe, guide in our attempts to determine the natural relations which exist between animals. This view of the subject seems to me, however, to circumscribe the foundation of a natural system of zoology and botany within too narrow limits, to exclude from our consideration some of the most striking characteristics of the two organic kingdoms of nature, and to leave it doubtful how far the arrangement thus obtained is founded in reality, and how far it is merely the expression of our estimate of these structural differences. It has appeared to me appropriate, therefore, to present here a short exposition of the leading features of the animal kingdom, as an introduction to the embryology of the chelonians, – one of the most extraordinary types among Vertebrata, – as it would afford a desirable opportunity of establishing a standard of comparison between the changes animals undergo during their growth, and the permanent characters of full-grown individuals of other types, and, perhaps, of showing also what other points beside structure might with advantage be considered in ascertaining the manifold relations of animals to one another and to the world in which they live, upon which the natural system may be founded.

In considering these various topics, I shall of necessity have to discuss many questions bearing upon the very origin of organized beings,

Reprinted from Contributions to the natural history of the United States of America, Vol. 1, Little Brown and Co., Boston (1857).

and to touch upon many points now under discussion among scientific men. I shall, however, avoid controversy as much as possible, and only try to render the results of my own studies and meditations in as clear a manner as I possibly can in the short space that I feel justified in devoting to this subject in this volume.

There is no question in natural history on which more diversified opinions are entertained than on that of classification; not that naturalists disagree as to the necessity of some sort of arrangement in describing animals or plants, for since nature has become the object of special studies, it has been the universal aim of all naturalists to arrange the objects of their investigations in the most natural order possible. Even Buffon, who began the publication of his great Natural History by denying the existence in nature of anything like a system, closed his work by grouping the birds according to certain general features, exhibited in common by many of them. It is true, authors have differed in their estimation of the characters on which their different arrangements are founded; and it is equally true that they have not viewed their arrangements in the same light, some having plainly acknowledged the artificial character of their systems, while others have urged theirs as the true expression of the natural relations which exist between the objects themselves. But, whether systems were presented as artificial or natural, they have, to this day, been considered generally as the expression of man's understanding of natural objects, and not as a system devised by the Supreme Intelligence and manifested in these objects.

There is only one point in these innumerable systems on which all seem to meet, namely, the existence in nature of distinct species, persisting with all their peculiarities, for a time at least; for even the immutability of species has been questioned. Beyond species, however, this confidence in the existence of the divisions, generally admitted in zoological systems, diminishes greatly.

With respect to genera, we find already the number of the naturalists who accept them as natural divisions much smaller; few of them having expressed a belief that genera have as distinct an existence in nature as species. And as to families, orders, classes, or any kind of higher divisions, they seem to be universally considered as convenient devices, framed with the view of facilitating the study of innumerable objects, and of grouping them in the most suitable manner. The indifference with which this part of our science is generally treated becomes unjustifiable, considering the progress which zoology in general has made of late. It is a matter of consequence whether genera are circumscribed in our systematic works within these or those limits; whether families inclose a wider or more contracted range of genera; whether such or such orders are admitted in a class, and what are the natural boundaries of classes; as well as how the classes themselves are related to one another, and whether all these groups are considered as resting upon the same foundation in nature or not.

Without venturing here upon an analysis of the various systems of zoology — the prominent features of which are sufficiently exemplified for my purpose by the systems of Linnæus and Cuvier, which must be familiar to every student of natural history — it is certainly a reasonable question to ask, whether the animal kingdom exhibits only those few subdivisions into orders and genera which the Linnæan system indicates, or whether the classes differ among themselves to the extent which the system of Cuvier would lead us to suppose. Or is, after all, this complicated structure of classification merely an ingenious human invention, which every one may shape, as he pleases, to suit himself? When we remember that all the works on natural history admit some system or other of this kind, it is certainly an aim worthy of a true naturalist to ascertain what is the real meaning of all these divisions.

Embryology, moreover, forces the inquiry upon us at every step, as it is impossible to establish precise comparisons between the different stages of growth of young animals of any higher group and the permanent characters of full-grown individuals of other types without first ascertaining what is the value of the divisions with which we may have to compare embryos. This is my reason for introducing here, in a work chiefly devoted to embryology, a subject to which I have paid the most careful attention for many years past, and for the solution of which I have made special investigations. . . .

33

a statistical study of the rattlesnakes

LAURENCE M. KLAUBER

. . . This is not a monograph of the rattlesnakes, nor an attempt particularly to unravel the problem of the genetic relationships of the species. Rather it is a tracing of the trends of a number of different variables through the group, for a survey of the dispersion of characteristics of form and lepidosis constitutes the essential object of the investigation. If, thereby, relationships are indicated or determined, incidental steps toward the solution of the taxonomic problems will result; but primarily the purpose has been to ascertain the extent and equations of the variations; how they cluster about the mean; and whether they are individual, sexual, or specific. It is hoped, also, that through this study of the rattlers, some indication may be given of the general value of certain morphological characters as differential indicators amongst the snakes, particularly those which are ordinarily employed in ophidian classification. I am duly aware that this is a presumptuous program upon the part of one who has had no formal training in either statistics or herpetology.

Always the searcher hopes to find, perhaps hidden in some inconspicuous character, a definite and invariable key, distinguishing or individualizing one form from all its relatives, as if nature had written here the technical name of that form. But usually what is available is only the cumulative evidence of many characters, few of which coincide at points of divergence. Some of these may be translated into the statistics

Reprinted with the author's and publisher's permission from Occasional Papers of the San Diego Society of Natural History, No. 1 (1936) and No. 4 (1938).

of average and correlation, and thereby serve, by weight of evidence rather than by rigid limits, to differentiate the forms. These cumulative weights are difficult to determine, and thus individual classificaton or group segregation becomes difficult. There is confusion between those variations produced by directional trends in form and others which are the result of individual or sexual differences. There are still other divergences, which, while definite as trends, are too unstable or too vague in value to warrant even the smallest definable distinction, that is, a division into subspecies or geographical races.

Differential characters may be of a type not describable as positive or negative, present or absent, nor in numerical or statistical form. An investigator of long experience with a certain animal notes automatically these differences and their cumulative effectiveness, or weight; but they are difficult to explain or evaluate for the use of other workers with less acquaintance with that particular genus or family.

Thus, the large series becomes important in order that the weight and dispersion of the many characters, which in summation constitute the basis of differentiation, can be followed through from the individual to a family or brood, thence to a localized group, then to collections of wider geographical range and varying habitat conditions, and thus to the classification of subspecies, species, and genus. Meanwhile the parallel differences due to sex and age must be noted and correlated with the others. By such studies the values of the several variants as key or reference characters may be determined.

This involves also a study of the relative stability of characters. Large series make it possible to determine averages of the numerical data with relatively small probable errors of the mean, that is, the errors inherent in random sampling. Having determined these, as well as the dispersions of the variates, we may next check the significance of the differences (for various characters) between two groups, such as members of the same subspecies from different geographical locations, or ecological niches, to see how far divergence has gone and which characters show the highest degree of plasticity or mobility, and which, conversely, of stability. These data in turn should aid in the evaluation of subspecific and specific differences, thus indicating, by composite weight, relationships and the validity of taxonomic separation; for it would seem that differences in stable characters should be given more weight in judging species differences than deviations in characters shown to be unstable within a species. . . .

We now proceed to work out some taxonomic problems involving head length to demonstrate the application of the method previously developed.

As we observe in captivity several cages of *Crotalus mitchellii,* some from the Cape Region of Lower California, others from San Diego County and western Arizona, it appears that the Mexican snakes have proportionately smaller heads than those from California; whether there is a difference between the San Diego County and Arizona material is uncertain. It is desired to determine whether these are real differences, or whether they are only imagined by the observer. Such differences, if present, are often more apparent in live than in preserved specimens.

We first survey the available material and find that moderately plentiful series of adults from each area are available. It appears that we can restrict the range to be included in our comparison to snakes no less than 700 nor more than 950 mm. in body length and still have adequate numbers. We decide on an approximate mid-point, or 850 mm. as the standard length at which the geographical groups will be compared. We now determine the regression equation for each group. . . . Standardized head lengths, thus computed for each available specimen, are then gathered into an array (separate for each geographical group which we are investigating), and their statistics are computed in the usual way. In the example *mitchellii* problem, we have the following:

	Cape San Lucas	Central Arizona	San Diego County
Number of specimens	45	18	29
Body length range, mm.	732-939	700-943	730-931
Standard body length, mm.	850	850	850
Mean head length equated to standard body length, mm.	32.04	39.33	39.24
Standard error of the mean, mm.	0.224	0.220	0.339
Standard deviation, mm.	1.50	0.93	1.82
Coefficient of variation, per cent	4.7	2.4	4.7

Using the ordinary formula to determine the standard error of the difference between the means of the parent populations, we find, comparing the San Diego County with the Cape San Lucas specimens, that the difference between the means (39.24 — 32.04 = 7.20 mm.) is more than seventeen times its standard error (0.412), which is, of course, highly significant. On the other hand, comparing the Arizona with the San Diego County specimens, we find a difference between the means of 0.09 mm. ± 0.411. Here the difference is only one-fourth of its standard error, and is, therefore, without significance. We reach the conclusion that, in head length proportionality, the Cape San Lucas specimens are significantly different from those of the other two areas (which do not differ from each other); and, especially if confirmed by other characteristics, at least a subspecific segregation is warranted. Thus, the revival of Cope's name *pyrrhus* for the southern California and Arizona specimens is justified. . . .

34

the concept of species based on experiment

JENS CLAUSEN, DAVID D. KECK,
and WILLIAM M. HIESEY

. . . Here is not the place to enter into a detailed discussion on the nature, composition and evolution of natural species. This is the subject of volumes in preparation based on our detailed experiments. It is sufficient here to state that plants are organized into groups, the members of each of which are able to interchange their genes freely in all proportions without detriment to the offspring. Such groups are separated from one another by internal barriers that are of a genetic-physiologic nature (including chromosomal barriers) that prevent such free interchange. These natural groups correspond fairly closely to the species of the moderately conservative taxonomists working with plants that reproduce sexually.

This criterion for species, now substantiated by experiment, is the same that Turesson previously applied to the ecospecies. Consequently, we use his terminology to distinguish species whose status has been determined by experiment. The ecospecies becomes the experimental homologue of the taxonomic species. Also Dobzhansky has recently called attention to the importance of the internal ("physiologic") barriers separating species, noting that commonly they coincide with the delimitations of the species as accepted by systematists.

For simplicity, the experimental concept of species has been put in tabular form. . . .

Reprinted with the authors' and publisher's permission from the American Journal of Botany, Vol. 26 (1939), pp. 103-106.

TABLE 1. *The concept of species.*[a]

<table>
<tr><th>Degree of separation
Internal / External</th><th>Hybrids fertile, second generation vigorous</th><th>Hybrids partially sterile, second generation weak</th><th>Hybrids sterile or none</th></tr>
<tr><td>In different environments</td><td>Distinct subspecies
ECOTYPES</td><td>Distinct species
ECOSPECIES</td><td rowspan="2">Distinct species complexes,
CENOSPECIES</td></tr>
<tr><td>In the same environment</td><td>Local variations of one species
BIOTYPES</td><td>Species overlapping in common territory (with hybrid swarms)</td></tr>
</table>

[a] The systematic units based on experimental evidence are in capitals, their homologues based on external characteristics are in italics.

The degree of separation used in this system of classification is based upon two kinds of barriers – internal (hereditary) and external (environmental). The internal barriers are possibly all genetic-physiologic, expressed through incompatibility and intersterility or through weakness of the hybrid offspring. Ultimately, it is probably the genes that govern the rates and inception of the metabolic processes that are so evidently off-balance in offspring of interspecific hybrids. The external barriers are either ecologic or geographic. A distinct geographic barrier is likely also to be ecologic. The most permanent barriers are the internal, because they persist even though the environment changes in a changing world. They are therefore used in distingushing species. A qualifying statement as to the internal barrier is necessary. Two forms may prove intersterile by direct test, although they interlink through one or several intermediaries that are interfertile with both. The barrier separating such forms is not considered specific, because genes may be exchanged through the intermediary.

Cenospecies – If the genetic barrier is absolute, it separates groups so perfectly that they are able to exist together in one environment without intermixing. This kind of barrier is characteristic for individuals belonging to different cenospecies or species complexes. The cenospecies are groups of major evolutionary importance, comparable to but not at all identical with the taxonomic section, and may contain from one to many ecospecies. Members of different cenospecies may cross, but the hybrids are sterile unless doubling of chromosomes (amphidiploidy) takes place, in which circumstance a new species has evolved — a new step in the evolutionary process.

ECOSPECIES — If the genetic isolation is only partial, we usually find that there is an additional geographic or ecologic isolation. This kind of separation, partly genetic and partly ecologic, is characteristic of ecospecies of one cenospecies. The ecospecies correspond to but are not always identical with the taxonomic species. To a limited extent, ecospecies of one cenospecies can exchange genes across the barriers, and they may show parallel variation on account of this exchange through the ages. If crossed, their hybrids are partially sterile, whereby nonviable sex cells are eliminated, or the second generation offspring is weak; most often both these conditions obtain. Weakness of the second generation may manifest itself in various ways: many individuals are slow-growing dwarfs, or subnormals; others are very susceptible to diseases to which the grandparents and even F_1 are immune; others again may be structural or anatomical misfits, to mention some examples. Any one or all of these weaknesses may characterize a hybrid population. In a world with strong competition such misfits have few chances of survival. A small percentage of the total offspring may be vigorous and fertile but tends to be eventually absorbed into one or the other of the parental species.

A group of ecospecies belonging to one cenospecies is found to inhabit a series of geographically or ecologically separated areas: one may inhabit a coastal region, another an inland region; one forested, the other open areas; one basic or alkaline, the other acid soils; one low, the other high altitudes; one a southern, the other a northern territory, and so on. In extreme cases, as in *Salix* or *Viola,* there may be as many as twenty or thirty ecospecies in one cenospecies. The genetic barriers between ecospecies are often produced by differences in number of chromosomes. Hybrid swarms may be found in nature where two ecospecies of one cenospecies meet or overlap.

ECOTYPE — If there is no genetic but only geographic or ecologic isolation, the units are considered ecotypes of one ecospecies. They parallel, but are not nearly always identical with, the geographic subspecies. Ecotypes of one ecospecies may occupy a series of different habitats similar to that mentioned under ecospecies. The only difference between the two units is the lack of a genetic barrier between ecotypes. Like ecospecies, they differ by many genes. They hybridize freely where they meet, but at a distance from the point of contact they are quite pure. Ecotypes are evidently the forerunners of ecospecies, and there is no absolute gap between the two. Only a few cases, however, are truly intermediate and difficult to classify, and they are but a small fraction of the doubtful cases that arise in classification based exclusively on external appearance. They are inevitable in a dynamic, changing world.

Principles and Application – Two factors that are of great importance for living things are taken into consideration in this classification: the environment in which the organism lives, and the heredity, which must fit in the environment. Differences in form, long taken as the sole basis in classification, are now understood as important only as they mark genetic differences of various sorts, including those which have proved of selective value when subjected to the environment.

Ecospecies, ecotypes, and local variations are all based upon hereditary differences, but only the former two show any correlation to the environment. Differences in heredity cannot be seen directly but must be established by experiment. The simplest experiment of this kind is to grow samples of natural populations in a uniform garden. This eliminates the gross environmental differences and makes it possible to compare the heredity. The analysis of the heredity, however, can be undertaken only by hybridization experiments.

The morphological characters which taxonomists use in their classification have often been discredited as being of no importance in the life of the plant. This may be correct if we consider the characters by themselves, but our experiments show that they may be closely correlated to the physiologic-hereditary complexes on which ecotypes are based, such as earliness and capacity for survival in certain environments. Also, there is often an absolute correlation between morphological characteristics and the chromosome number or other internal barriers that separate species. When experiments have established the correlations, such character complexes become important indicators or key characters that can be used in tracing the distribution of ecotypes and ecospecies in the field and in mapping them with the aid of herbaria. . . .

35

plant phenolics as taxonomic guides

E. C. BATE-SMITH

Except for the anthocyanin pigments of flower petals, little thought is given by botanists to the phenolic constituents of plants; and this in spite of their presence in all of the higher and most of the lower plants, and the often surprising concentrations of them present in the living tissues. The reason for this lack of interest is, no doubt, that no function can, in general, be ascribed to them, and no explanation can be given for their extraordinary diversity. Both their universal presence and this very diversity suggest, however, that it would be well worth while seeking for some sign of regularity in their distribution. A search for signs of regularity is, in fact, very soon rewarded, and I am going to try to describe some of the early results of such a search. . . .

THE COMMONER PHENOLIC CONSTITUENTS

It emerges from this survey that three classes of phenolic constituents overwhelmingly predominate in the leaves of vascular plants: leucoanthocyanins, flavonols, and hydroxycinnamic acids. These, and also a great many of the less common plant phenolics, are closely related chemically, having in common a benzene ring carrying one, two or three hydroxyl groups and a three-carbon unsaturated side chain. . . . We shall be especially concerned with eight of these common types, two leucoanthocyanins, two flavonols, three cinnamic acid derivatives, and a fourth substance, ellagic acid. . . .

Reprinted with the author's and publisher's permission from the Proceedings of the Linnaean Society of London, Vol. 169 (1958), pp. 198-211.

THE NOT-SO-COMMON PHENOLIC CONSTITUENTS

For the most part, these can be regarded as progressively less oxidized counterparts of the commoner types. Thus the catechins are less oxidized, by the equivalent of one hydroxyl group, than the leucoanthocyanins; the flavones, and flavanonols similarly, in relation to the flavonols, and the flavanones and chalkones still further reduced by one hydroxyl equivalent. The aurones, at the same level of oxidation as the flavones, are ring-closed to form a five-membered ring, the *iso*-flavones are substituted at carbon atom 3 instead of at carbon atom 2. One important variation is the absence of a hydroxyl group on carbon atom 5 – we ourselves for brevity call such compounds "5-anoxy" compounds. They seem likely to be particularly useful in systematic diagnosis, since they are, as a class, brilliantly flourescent. . . .

The genus *Iris* affords an opportunity not only of examining the way in which differences between species of a single genus reflect the morphological differences on which the division of the genus has been based, but also the situation in monocotyledons generally. Table 8 gives the results which have been obtained for members of seven of the twelve sections into which the genus is divided by Dykes, one of these, the Apogon section, being further divided into eight subsections and a miscellaneous group.

TABLE 8. Distribution of phenolics in sections of *Iris*.

				Apogon										
	Reticulata	Juno	Pardanthopsis	Sibirica	Spuria	Californica	Hexagona	Laevigata (*Pseudacorus*)	Foetidissima	Unguicularis	Ensata	Regelia	Evansia	Pogoniris
Leuco-anthocyanins	−	−	−	+	+	+	−	+	−	−	−	+	−	−
Flavonols	−	−	−	+	−	+	−	−	−	−	−	−	−	−
Caffeic acid	−	−	−	+ −	(+) −	+	+	−	(+)	(+)	−	+	−	−
Methoxy-acids	?	+	+	+	+	+	+	−	+	+	+	+	+	+
*iso*Flavones (rhizome)	−	−	−	−	−	−	−	−	−	−	−	−	+	+

In general, the universal presence of the methoxy acids is to be noted. Next, the biochemical similarity between the Evansia and Pogoniris sections, regarded as equivalent eastern and western groups, respectively. Third, the co-occurrence of leuco-anthocyanins with flavonols and caffeic acid and the virtual restriction of these to the one (Apogon) section. As a point of special interest, the position of the species *I. flavissima* Palt. included in the Pogoniris section by Dykes, was questioned by Simonet on the grounds of its anomalous chromosome number, and its placing is equally to be doubted on biochemical grounds. Its phenolic constitution would agree with its inclusion in the Regelia section, the position preferred by Simonet, and now adopted by the Iris Society.

The biochemical variation within the genus is considerable, but no more so than the variation in such important respects as the bulbous and rhizomatous nature of the root system. There is no distinction here as between woody and herbaceous forms, and this is quite general in the monocotyledons. In this class the herbaceous habit is so predominant that distinctions other than those associated with the woody and herbaceous habit come more clearly into evidence. One such distinction is that between aquatic or marshy as opposed to the terrestrial habitat. In the genus *Iris,* for instance, it is in the leaves of the moisture-loving species in the Apogon section that leuco-anthocyanins are found, and this appears to be fairly general for the monocotyledons as a whole. . . .

REASONS FOR REGARDING THE PHENOLIC CONSTITUENTS AS A BIOCHEMICALLY PRIVILEGED CLASS

The first reason for taking this view is that the phenolic compounds appear to be metabolically inert. They are formed in the living cell in considerable amounts, and nothing, so far as is known, happens to them in the living cell but to be laid down in the cell wall. The phenolic compounds found in the living tissues are, therefore, stable and characteristic end products.

The second reason is that the chain of biosynthetic processes leading to their formation appears to be irreversible from the point where quinic acid (which, it will be remembered, is richly present in combination with the hydroxy-aromatic acids) is converted through shikimic acid to the first true aromatic residue. There seems to be a narrow channel into a closed area of biosynthesis from which the only escape route is total oxidation.

Within this area, however, the forms assumed by the end products of synthesis can be many and various. Usually the forms found in the less woody plants differ from those in the more woody ones by being less oxidized: flavones, aurones and chalkones rather than flavonols; or more methylated: methoxy acids rather than hydroxy acids. The extent of such differences is, however, rigidly defined for the species, so that the phenolic compounds present in the tissues are characteristic of the species, and are often shared by species of the same genus or family. These conclusions pose significant questions for the physiologist both as regards the mechanism of the synthetic processes at work in the plant cell and as regards the function of the phenolic constituents in the life of the plant. Answers to these questions must be important to the taxonomist because they will go a long way towards supplying the *reasons* for the morphological differences on which his systems of classification are based. In the meantime, there are already a number of guides to classification in the precise array of phenolic substances which a plant is able to fabricate, and which the biochemist can now so easily identify. . . .

Origin of Life

The nature of the beginning of life has occupied a central position in man's insatiable quest for explanation. Creation theory, i.e., origin through divine intervention, is extant in all the major religions and provides satisfaction for all but those who seek causality explicated by rationality rather than faith. Not incompatible with this concept were putative reports of horse hairs in rain barrels generating into horsehair worms, or of exposed meat organizing maggots *de novo*. Such repeated spontaneous generation of the animate from the inanimate could, by relative ease, be compatible with the idea of a divine being directing such events.

As early as 1688, Redi devised a series of elegant experiments which challenged the *de novo* origin of living things (p. 132). Yet another hundred years passed, however, before Spallanzani (p. 135) corroborated Redi's findings. In spite of these truly remarkable experiments by Redi and Spallanzani, it was not until the 1860s that the theory of spontaneous generation was completely discredited. This occurred in debate before the French Academy of Science which had proposed a prize for the occasion. It was here that the trenchant analysis of Louis Pasteur laid the death blow to the prevailing theory (p. 138). The paradox to which this led, however, was that if spontaneous generation were inadequate to explain the origin of life, then divine intervention must be involved. This is an untestable and hence improper scientific hypothesis.

The resolution of the dilemma came in a book by the Russian biochemist A. I. Oparin in 1925 (p. 141). When his study was translated into English in 1938 it found quite rapid support among the intellectual community. Oparin's hypothesis was largely speculative but has seen corroboration in a number of investigations and observations made subsequently. Foremost among these was Miller's report in 1953 of the production in the laboratory of two of the most ubiquitous amino acids under primitive earth atmosphere conditions (p. 145). Fox has shown the possibility of thermal energy as an alternate molecular-forming process (p. 148) and has made a number of intriguing observations of the "life-like" behavior of macromolecules produced in this way.

Perhaps the most exciting aspect of studies on the origin of life lies in the speculation they allow regarding extraterrestrial life. If the genesis of life is explicable as a natural phenomenon, and appropriate conditions obtain elsewhere in the universe, it follows that some kind of organized biological entities are to be expected as man explores the universe. The expansion of man's horizon has barely begun.

36

experiments on the generation of insects

FRANCESCO REDI

. . . In the meanwhile I had placed in a glass dish some skinned river frogs, and having left the dish open, I found the next day, on examination, that some small worms were occupied in devouring them, while some others swam about, at the bottom of the dish, in a watery matter that had run out of the frogs. The next day the worms had all increased in size and many others had appeared that also swam below and on top of the water, where they devoured the floating fragments of flesh; and after two days, having consumed all that was left of the frogs, they swam and sported about in the fetid liquid, now creeping up, all soft and slimy, on the side of the glass, now wriggling back to the water until at last on the following day, without my knowledge, they all disappeared, having reached the top of the dish.

At the same time I enclosed some fish, called Barbi, in a box full of holes, with a lid perforated in the same way. When I opened it after four hours, I found a large number of very minute maggots on the fish, and I saw a great many tiny eggs adhering in bunches to the joints and around all the holes in the interior of the box: some of these were white and others yellow. I crushed them between my nails, and the cracked shell emitted a kind of whitish liquid, thinner and less viscous than the white of a fowl's egg.

Having rearranged the box as it was before, and having opened it, on the following day, I observed that all the eggs had hatched into the

Reprinted from the translation of Mab Bigelow, Open Court Publishing Co., Chicago (1909).

same number of maggots, and that the empty shells were still attached in the places where the hatching occurred; I also noted that the first maggots hatched had increased to double their size; but what surprised me most was that on the following day they had grown so large that every one of them weighed about seven grains, while only the day before there would have been twenty-four or thirty to a grain. All the later ones hatched were very small. The whole lot, almost in the twinkling of an eye, finished devouring the flesh of the fish, leaving all the bones so clean and white that they looked like skeletons polished by the hand of the most skillful anatomist.

All these maggots, having been placed where they could not escape in spite of all their endeavors, five or six days after birth turned as usual into as many eggs [pupæ], some of red and some of black color, and not of the same size; subsequently, at the proper time, different kinds of flies came out, green flies, big blue flies, black flies striped with white, and others resembling the marine locust and winged ants, which I have described. Besides these four kinds I also saw eight or ten common flies, such as daily hover and buzz about our dinner tables.

Having on the twentieth day noticed that among the larger eggs [pupæ], there were some still unhatched, I separated them from the others in a different vessel, and two days after there gradually came out of them some very small gnats, the number of which after two days had greatly exceeded the number of eggs [pupæ]. I opened the vessel and having broken five or six of the eggs [pupæ] I found them so packed with gnats that each shell held at least twenty-five or thirty, and at most forty. . . .

Having considered these things, I began to believe that all worms found in meat were derived directly from the droppings of flies, and not from the putrefaction of the meat, and I was still more confirmed in this belief by having observed that, before the meat grew wormy, flies had hovered over it, of the same kind as those that later bred in it. Belief would be vain without the confirmation of experiment, hence in the middle of July I put a snake, some fish, some eels of the Arno, and a slice of milk-fed veal in four large, wide-mouthed flasks; having well closed and sealed them, I then filled the same number of flasks in the same way, only leaving these open. It was not long before the meat and the fish, in these second vessels, became wormy and flies were seen entering and leaving at will; but in the closed flasks I did not see a worm, though many days had passed since the dead flesh had been put in them. Outside on the paper cover there was now and then a deposit, or a maggot that eagerly sought some crevice by which to enter and obtain nourishment. Meanwhile the different things placed in the flasks had become putrid and stinking; the fish, their bones excepted, had all been dissolved into a thick, turbid fluid, which on settling became clear, with a drop or so of liquid grease floating on the surface; but the snake kept its form intact, with the same color, as if it had been put in but yesterday; the eels, on the contrary, produced little liquid, though they had become very much swollen, and losing all shape, looked like a viscous mass of glue; the veal, after many weeks, became hard and dry.

Not content with these experiments, I tried many others at different seasons, using different vessels. In order to leave nothing undone, I even had pieces of meat put underground, but though remaining buried for weeks, they never bred worms, as was always the case when flies had been allowed to light on the meat. One day a large number of worms, which had bred in some buffalo meat, were killed by my order; having placed part in a closed dish, and part in an open one, nothing appeared in the first dish, but in the second worms had hatched, which changing as usual into egg-shape balls [pupæ], finally became flies of the common kind. In the same experiment tried with dead flies, I never saw anything breed in the closed vessel. . . .

Leaving this long digression and returning to my argument, it is necessary to tell you that although I thought I had proved that the flesh of dead animals could not engender worms unless the semina of live ones were deposited therein, still, to remove all doubt, as the trial had been made with closed vessels into which the air could not penetrate or circulate, I wished to attempt a new experiment by putting meat and fish in a large vase closed only with a fine Naples veil, that allowed the air to enter. For further protection against flies, I placed the vessel in a frame covered with the same net. I never saw any worms in the meat, though many were to be seen moving about on the net-covered frame. These, attracted by the odor of the meat, succeeded at last in penetrating the fine meshes and would have entered the vase had I not speedily removed them. It was interesting, in the meanwhile, to notice the number of flies buzzing about which, every now and then, would light on the outside net and deposit worms there. I noted that some left six or seven at a time there, and others dropped them in the air before reaching the net. Perhaps these were of the same breed mentioned by Scaliger, in whose hand, by a lucky accident, a large fly deposited some small worms, whence he drew the conclusion that all flies bring forth live worms directly and not eggs. But what I have already said on the subject proves how much this learned man was in error. It is true that some kinds of flies bring forth live worms and some others eggs, as I have proved by experiment. . . .

37

observations and experiments upon the animalcula of infusions

LAZARO SPALLANZANI

I hermetically sealed vessels with the eleven kinds of seeds mentioned before [kidney beans, vetches, buckwheat, barley, maize, mallow, beet, peas, lentils, beans, hemp]. To prevent the rarefaction of the internal air, I diminished the thickness of the necks of the vessels, till they terminated in tubes almost capillary, and, putting the smallest part to the blowpipe, sealed it instantaneously, so that the internal air underwent no alteration. It was necessary to know whether the seeds might suffer by this inclusion, which might be an obstacle to the production of animalcula. Other experiments had shewn me, (1) vessels hermetically sealed have no animalcula, unless they are very capacious: (2) animalcula are not always produced; (3) when they are produced, the number is never so great as in open vessels. Although I used pretty large vessels, two substances, peas and beans, had not a single animalcule. The other nine afforded a sufficient number; and to these I limited my experiments. I took nine vessels with seeds, hermetically sealed. I immersed them in boiling water for half a minute. I immersed another nine for a whole minute, nine more for a minute and a half; and nine for two minutes. Thus, I had thirty-six infusions. That I might know the proper time to examine them, I made similar infusions in open vessels, and, when these swarmed with animalcula, I opened those hermetically sealed. Upon breaking the seal of the first, I found the elasticity of the air encreased. Seeds contain much air; a great quantity should escape

Reprinted from the translation (translator unknown) of Tracts on the nature of animals and vegetables, Edinburgh (1799).

in their dissolution, by heat or maceration, which must, of necessity, render the portion of included air denser and more elastic. However, the elasticity may originate partly from the elastic fluid discovered in vegetables, the nature of which is apparently different from the atmospheric fluid. I examined the infusions, and was surprised to find some of them an absolute desert; others reduced to such a solitude that but a few animalcula, like points, were seen, and their existence could be discovered only with the greatest difficulty. The action of heat for one minute was as injurious to the production of the animalcula as of two. The seeds producing the inconceivably small animalcula were beans, vetches, buckwheat, mallows, maize, and lentils. I could never discover the least animation in the other three infusions. I thence concluded that the heat of boiling water for half a minute was fatal to all animalcula of the largest kind; even to the middle-sized, and the smallest, of those which I shall term animalcula of the higher class, to use the energetic expression of M. Bonnet; while the heat of two minutes did not affect those I shall place in the lower class.

Having hermetically sealed six vessels, containing six kinds of seeds producing animalcula of the lower class, I immersed them in boiling water for two minutes and a half, three, three and a half, and four minutes. The seals of twenty-four vessels being broken at a suitable time, there were no animalcula of the higher class seen, but more or fewer of the lower. The air was almost always condensed, both in this and in the other experiments.

In vessels immersed seven minutes, I found animalcula of the lower class. They appeared in vessels immersed twelve minutes.

The minuteness of animalcula of the lower class does not prevent our distinguishing the difference of their figure and proportions.

Boiling half an hour was no obstacle to the production of animalcula of the lower class; but boiling for three quarters, or even less, deprived all the six infusions of animalcula.

We know that the heat of boiling water is about 212°. These infusions were of this heat at least, as appeared by the marks they exhibited of ebullition, the whole time the surrounding water boiled. Philosophers know that water, boiled in a close vessel, acquires a greater degree of heat than when boiled in an open. To know how much less than half a minute the boiling might be abridged, an animalcula of the higher class yet exist, I made use of a second pendulum, and immersed the vessels in boiling water for a given number of seconds, beginning with 29. In a word, boiling for a single second prevented their existence. . . .

Two important consequences thence arise. The first evinces the extreme efficacy of heat to deprive infusions in closed vessels of a multitude of animated beings; for, in open vessels, are always seen a vast concourse of animalcula. The second consequence concerns the constancy of animalcula of the lower class appearing in infusions boiled in close vessels; and the heat of 212°, protracted an hour, has been no obstacle to their existence. . . .

We are therefore induced to believe that those animalcula originate from germs there included, which, for a certain time, withstand the effects of heat, but at length yield under it; and, since animalcula of the higher classes only exist when the heat is less intense, we must imagine they are much sooner affected by it than those of the lower classes. Whence we should conclude that this multitude of the superior animalcula, seen in the infusions of open vessels, exposed not only to the heat of boiling water, but to the flame of a blowpipe, appears there, not because their germs have withstood so great a degree of heat, but because new germs come to the infusions after cessation of the heat. . . .

The idea that animalcula come from the air appears to me to be confirmed by undoubted facts. I took sixteen large and equal glass vases: four I sealed hermetically; four were stopped with a wooden stopper, well fitted; four with cotton; and the four last I left open. In each of the four classes of vases were hempseed, rice, lentils, and peas. The infusions were boiled a full hour before being put into the vases. I began the experiments 11. May, and visited the vases 5. June. In each there were two kinds of animalcula, large and small; but in the four open ones, they were so numberous and confused that the infusions, if I may use the expression, rather seemed to teem with life. In those stoppered with cotton, they were about a third more rare; still fewer in those with wooden stoppers; and much more so in those hermetically sealed.

The number of animalcula developed is proportioned to the communication with the external air. The air either conveys the germs to the infusions, or assists the expansion of those already there. . . .

38

memoir on the organized bodies which exist in the atmosphere; examination of the doctrine of spontaneous generation

LOUIS PASTEUR

Thus when, subsequently to the studies I have just related, a competent naturalist of Rouen, Monsieur Pouchet, corresponding member of the Académie des Sciences, announced to the Académie results upon which he believed he was able to base in a definitive way the principle of spontaneous generation, no one could point out the real source of error of his experiments; and soon the Académie, comprehending what remained to be studied, proposed for the subject of a prize the following question:

To attempt, by well-constituted experiments, to shed new light on the question of spontaneous generation.

The question then appeared so obscure that Monsieur Biot, whose benevolence has never been lacking in my studies, regretfully saw me engaged in these studies, and demanded, in deference to his advice, the acceptance of a limited time beyond which I would abandon the subject if I were not past master of the difficulties which engaged me. Monsieur Dumas, whose benevolence often augmented that which came to me from Monsieur Biot, said to me at the same time, "I would not advise anyone to remain with this subject for very much time." . . .

At the point which I had reached in my studies on fermentation, I was obliged to form an opinion on the question of spontaneous generation. I would perhaps be able to hit upon a powerful argument in favor of my ideas on fermentations themselves.

Reprinted from the Annales de Chimie et de Physique, Vol. 64 (1862), pp. 1-110. Translated by Edward J. Kormondy, 1965.

The research given here was consequently but a digression necessitated by my studies on fermentations.

It is thus that I was brought to be occupied with a subject which until then had exercised only the sagacity of naturalists.

My first problem was to find a method to permit collecting in any season the solid particles which float in the air and study them under the microscope. It was necessary at first to eliminate, insofar as possible, the objections which partisans of spontaneous generation oppose to the ancient hypothesis of aerial dissemination of germs. . . .

The procedure which I have followed to collect dust suspended in the air and to examine with the microscope is of great simplicity: it consists of filtering a measured volume of air through gun cotton which is soluble in a mixture of alcohol and ether. The cotton fibers arrest the solid particles. The cotton is then dissolved. After a sufficiently prolonged pause, all the solid particles fall to the bottom of the liquid; after being washed several times, they are placed on the microscope stage, where their study is facilitated. . . .

Using ordinary methods, they can be treated with different reagents: iodine solution, potash, sulfuric acid, stains.

These exceedingly simple manipulations permit recognition that there is constantly in ordinary air a variable number of bodies whose form and structure indicate that they are organized. Their dimensions range from the smallest diameters to 1/100 - 1.5/100 mm and more. Some are perfectly spherical, others ovoid. Their contours are more or less distinctly outlined. Many are completely translucent, but some are opaque with granulations inside. Those which are translucent with distinct contours so closely resemble spores of the most common molds that the most skillful microscopist would not see the difference. . . . But as for affirming that this is a spore, let alone the spore of a particular species, and that this is an egg and the egg of such and such a microorganism, I believe that not to be possible. I confine myself to that which concerns me — to declare that these bodies are evidently organized, resembling in all respects the germs of lowest organisms, and so diverse in volume and structure that they obviously belong to a great number of species. . . .

I believe I have rigorously established in the preceding chapters that all the organized bodies of infusions previously heated have no other origin than the solid particles which the air always carries and which it constantly allows to be deposited on all objects. If there could still remain the least doubt of the reader in this regard, it would be removed by the experiments I shall now relate.

I place in a glass flask one of the following liquids, each extremely alterable upon contact with ordinary air — solution of yeast of beer, sugar solution of yeast of beer, urine, sugar beet juice, pepper water; I then draw out the neck of the flask in a flame in such a way as to produce various curvatures. . . . I then bring the liquid to a boil for several minutes until steam issues copiously from the open tapered end of the neck, without any other precaution. I then allow the flask to cool. Remarkably, calculated to astonish all those accustomed to the delicacy of experiments relating to so-called spontaneous generation, the solution in the flask remains unaltered indefinitely. It may be handled without any fear, moved about from place to place, subjected to all variations of seasonal temperatures, and the liquid does not undergo the slightest alteration and conserves its odor and flavor. . . . There is no other change in its nature save that which might be produced, in a certain case, by a direct oxidation, purely chemical, of the substance . . . *at no time is there a production of organized bodies in the solution.*

It might seem that ordinary air, entering with force in the first moments, might reach the flask in a crude state. This is true, but it encounters a liquid still near boiling temperature. The entry of the air then takes place more slowly, and when the liquid is cooled enough so as not to remove vitality from the germs, the entering air is sufficiently retarded so that it deposits in the moist bends of the neck all the dust capable of acting upon the infusions and there causing organized bodies. At least, I do not see any other possible explanation for these curious experiments. For if, after one or more months in the incubator, the neck of the flask is detached by a stroke of a file, without otherwise touching the flask, after 24, 26 or 28 hours, mold and infusoria begin to appear exactly as ordinarily, or as if the flask were inoculated with dust from the air. . . .

I do not know anything more convincing than these experiments so easily repeated and which can be varied in a thousand ways. . . .

This granted, will a partisan of spontaneous generation continue to maintain his principles, even in the presence of these two propositions? He can still do so; but then his reasoning must of necessity be as follows, and I let the reader be the judge of it:

"There are in the air," he will say, "solid particles, such as calcium carbonate, silica, soot, fibers of wool, cotton, dirt, . . . , and side by side organized bodies of perfect resemblance to the spores of molds and the eggs of infusoria. Well, I prefer to place the origin of molds and infusoria in the first amorphous bodies group than in the second."

In my opinion, the inconsistency of such reasoning is self-evident. The entire progress of my research consists in having brought to bay the adherents of the doctrine of spontaneous generation. . . .

39

the origin of life

A. I. OPARIN

Summarizing what has been discussed in the preceding chapters, one must first of all categorically reject every attempt to renew the old arguments in favor of a sudden and spontaneous generation of life. It must be understood that no matter how minute an organism may be or how elementary it may appear at first glance it is nevertheless infinitely more complex than any simple solution of organic substances. It possesses a definite dynamically stable structural organization which is founded upon a harmonious combination of strictly coordinated chemical reactions. It would be senseless to expect that such an organization could originate accidentally in a more or less brief span of time from simple solutions or infusions.

However, this need not lead us to the conclusion that there is an absolute and fundamental difference between a living organism and lifeless matter. Everyday experience enables one to differentiate living things from their nonliving environment. But the numerous attempts to discover some specific "vital energies" resident only in organisms invariably ended in total failure, as the history of biology in the nineteenth and twentieth centuries teaches us.

That being the case, life could not have existed always. The complex combination of manifestations and properties so characteristic of life must have arisen in the process of evolution of matter. A weak attempt

Reprinted with the author's and translator's permission from the translation by Sergius Morgulis, The Macmillan Co., New York (1938).

has been made in these pages to draw a picture of this evolution without losing contact with the ground of scientifically established facts.

The gaseous mass which had once separated from the Sun, owing to a cosmic catastrophe, furnished the material out of which our planet was formed. Carbon together with other elements of the solar atmosphere passed into this gaseous mass which ultimately was destined to form our Earth. . . .

Mixed with the heavy metals, the carbon reacted chemically as the Earth gradually cooled off, whereby carbides were produced, which are the carbon compounds most stable at high temperatures. The crust of primary igneous rocks which were formed subsequently separated the carbides from the Earth's atmosphere. The atmosphere at that period differed materially from our present atmosphere in that it contained neither oxygen nor nitrogen gas but was filled instead with superheated aqueous vapor. The crust separating the carbides from this atmosphere still lacked rigidity to resist the gigantic tides of the inner molten liquid mass, caused by the attractive forces of Sun and Moon. The thin layer of igneous rock would rupture during these tides and through the crevices so formed the molten liquid mass from the interior depths would spread over the Earth's surface. The superheated aqueous vapor of the atmosphere coming in contact with the carbides reacted chemically giving rise to the simplest organic matter, the hydrocarbons, which in turn gave rise to a great variety of derivatives (alcohols, aldehydes, ketones, organic acids, etc.) through oxidation by the oxygen component of water. At the same time these hydrocarbons also reacted with ammonia which appeared at that period on the surface of the Earth. Thus amides, amines and other nitrogenous derivatives originated.

Thus it came about, when our planet had cooled off sufficiently to allow the condensation of aqueous vapor and the formation of the first envelope of hot water around the Earth, that this water already contained in solution organic substances, the molecules of which were made up of carbon, hydrogen, oxygen and nitrogen. These organic substances are endowed with tremendous chemical potentialities, and they entered a variety of chemical reactions not only with each other but also with the elements of the water itself. As a consequence of these reactions complex, high-[weight] molecular organic compounds were produced similar to those which at the present time comprise the organism of animals and plants. By this process also the biologically most important compounds, the proteins, must have originated.

At first these substances were present in the waters of seas and oceans in the form of colloidal solutions. Their molecules were dispersed and uniformly distributed in the solvent, but entirely inseparable from the dispersing medium. But as the colloidal solutions of various substances were mixed new and special formations resulted, the so-called coacervates or semiliquid colloidal gels. In this process organic substance becomes concentrated in definite spatial arrangements and separated from the solvent medium by a more or less distinct membrane. Inside these coacervates or gels the colloidal particles assume a definite position towards each other; in other words, the beginnings of some elementary structure appear in them. Each coacervate droplet acquires a certain degree of individuality and its further fate is now determined not only by the conditions of the external medium but also by its own specific internal physico-chemical structure. This internal structure of the droplet determined its ability to absorb with greater or less speed and to incorporate into itself organic substances dissolved in the surrounding water. This resulted in an increase of the size of the droplet, i.e., they acquired the power to grow. But the rate of growth depends upon the internal physico-chemical structure of a given colloidal system and is greater the more this is adapted for absorption and for the chemical transformation of the absorbed materials.

In such manner a peculiar situation had arisen which may be described as the growth competition of coacervate gels. However, the physico-chemical structure of gels during growth did not remain unaltered but tended constantly to change owing to the addition of new substances, to chemical interaction, etc. These transformations could either result in a further perfection of the organization or, on the contrary, induce the degradation and loss of structure. In other words, it could bring about self-destruction and resolution of the coacervate droplet which was itself responsible for starting the process. Only such changes in the structure of colloidal systems which enabled the gel to adsorb dissolved substances more rapidly and thus to grow better; in other words, only changes of a progressive kind acquired importance for continued existence and development. A peculiar selective process had thus come into play which finally resulted in the origin of colloidal systems with a highly developed physico-chemical organization, namely, the simplest primary organisms. . . .

Natural selection has long ago destroyed and completely wiped off the face of the Earth all the intermediate forms of organization of primary colloidal systems and of the simplest living things and, wherever the external conditions are favorable to the evolution of life, we find countless numbers of fully developed highly organized living things. If organic matter would appear at the present time it could not evolve for very long because it would be quickly consumed and destroyed by the innumerable microorganisms inhabiting the earth, water, and air.

For this reason, the process of evolution of organic substance, the process of formation of life sketched in the preceding pages cannot be observed directly now. The tremendously long intervals of time separating the single steps in this process make it impossible to reproduce the process as it occurred in nature under available laboratory conditions. . . .

40

a production of amino acids under possible primitive earth conditions

STANLEY L. MILLER

The idea that the organic compounds that serve as the basis of life were formed when the earth had an atmosphere of methane, ammonia, water, and hydrogen instead of carbon dioxide, nitrogen, oxygen, and water was suggested by Oparin and has been given emphasis recently by Urey and Bernal.

In order to test this hypothesis, an apparatus was built to circulate CH_4, NH_3, H_2O, and H_2 past an electric discharge. The resulting mixture has been tested for amino acids by paper chromatography. Electrical discharge was used to form free radicals instead of ultraviolet light, because quartz absorbs wave lengths short enough to cause photo-dissociation of the gases. Electrical discharge may have played a significant role in the formation of compounds in the primitive atmosphere.

. . . Water is boiled in the flask, mixes with the gases in the 5-l flask, circulates past the electrodes, condenses and empties back into the boiling flask. The U-tube prevents circulation in the opposite direction. The acids and amino acids formed in the discharge, not being volatile, accumulate in the water phase. The circulation of the gases is quite slow, but this seems to be an asset, because production was less in a different apparatus with an aspirator arrangement to promote circulation. The discharge, a small corona, was provided by an induction coil designed for detection of leaks in vacuum apparatus.

Reprinted with the author's and publisher's permission from Science, Vol. 117 (1953), pp. 528-529.

The experimental procedure was to seal off the opening in the boiling flask after adding 200 ml of water, evacuate the air, add 10 cm pressure of H_2, 20 cm of CH_4, and 20 cm of NH_3. The water in the flask was boiled, and the discharge was run continuously for a week.

During the run the water in the flask became noticeably pink after the first day, and by the end of the week the solution was deep red and turbid. Most of the turbidity was due to colloidal silica from the glass. The red color is due to organic compounds adsorbed on the silica. Also present are yellow organic compounds, of which only a small fraction can be extracted with ether, and which form a continuous streak tapering off at the bottom on a one-dimensional chromatogram run in butanol-acetic acid. These substances are being investigated further.

At the end of the run the solution in the boiling flask was removed and 1 ml of saturated $HgCl_2$ was added to prevent the growth of living organisms. The ampholytes were separated from the rest of the constituents by adding $Ba(OH)_2$ and evaporating *in vacuo* to remove amines, adding H_2SO_4 and evaporating to remove the acids, neutralizing with $Ba(OH)_2$, filtering and concentrating *in vacuo.*

The amino acids are not due to living organisms because their growth would be prevented by the boiling water during the run, and by the $HgCl_2$, $Ba(OH)_2$, H_2SO_4 during the analysis.

. . . Identification of an amino acid was made when the R_f value (the ratio of the distance traveled by the amino acid to the distance traveled by the solvent front), the shape, and the color of the spot were the same on a known, unknown, and mixture of the known and unknown; and when consistent results were obtained with chromatograms using phenol and 77% ethanol.

On this basis glycine, α-alanine and β-alanine are identified. The identification of the aspartic acid and *a*-amino-*n*-butyric acid is less certain because the spots are quite weak. The spots marked A and B are unidentified as yet, but may be beta and gamma amino acids. These are the main amino acids present, and others are undoubtedly present but in smaller amounts. It is estimated that the total yield of amino acids was in the milligram range.

In this apparatus an attempt was made to duplicate a primitive atmosphere of the earth, and not to obtain the optimum conditions for the formation of amino acids. Although in this case the total yield was small for the energy expended, it is possible that, with more efficient apparatus (such as mixing of the free radicals in a flow system, use of higher hydrocarbons from natural gas or petroleum, carbon dioxide, etc., and optimum ratios of gases), this type of process would be a way of commercially producing amino acids.

A more complete analysis of the amino acids and other products of the discharge is now being performed and will be reported in detail shortly.

41

experiments in molecular evolution and criteria of extraterrestrial life

SIDNEY W. FOX

. . . Of particular interest in an evolutionary context is the recent finding that almost all of the proteinaceous amino acids, and essentially no others, are formed by thermal synthesis from the Oparin-Urey "primordial" atmosphere. A thermal synthesis of amino acids was attempted because of the earlier finding that some proportion of each of the 18 to 20 amino acids common to protein could be found in appropriately synthesized anhydrocopolymers of those amino acids, by a thermal process. . . .

This kind of anhydrocopolymerization was accomplished; the conditions necessary for anhydrocopolymerization of 18 amino acids have been reviewed many times and the properties of such polymers have been recited many times. . . . Of first interest are the facts that the polymers contain all of the common proteinaceous amino acids, the moderately purified polymer is hydrolyzable quantitatively to amino acids, and that mean molecular weights are many thousand, ranging up to 10,000.

The polymers are split by proteolytic enzymes, particularly pepsin; they have nutritive quality for *Lactobacillus arabinosus* and for rats; the residues are distributed in the chains in a nonrandom, i.e., nonuniform, manner; they are found to have only a small proportion of cross-linking; and they have catalytic activity for the hydrolysis of *p*-nitrophenyl ace-

Reprinted with the author's permission from BioScience, Vol. 14 (1964), pp. 13-21.

tate, an unnatural substrate which has been much used by those working with enzyme models.

The most salient new information on the *proteinoids* concerns their ability to catalyze weakly the conversion of natural substrates as established first with radioactive glucose. The glucose is broken down to glucuronic acid which is then also decarboxylated by the proteinoid.

The developing picture from many such studies now under way is one of a number of weak catalytic activities, some stronger than others, in the proteinoids. This kind of behavior is consistent with the interpretation that the proteinoid is akin to primordial matter from which more specialized, more powerful enzymes evolved during evolution of molecules in organisms. . . .

Oparin, also, has recognized the principle of self-organizing properties of macromolecules as a natural solution to this problem; his major experimental effort has been with coacervate droplets as models of cells. These droplets are lacking in stability comparable to that of cells. They are, moreover, crucially deficient as models of precellular organization in that they are made from materials produced by cells. Solution of a basic dilemma in the theory of the origin of life requires that the material arise in the absence of life.

Accordingly, the most significant property of the proteinoids (and other thermal poly-α-amino acids) may well be their propensity to form huge numbers of microspheres in the coccoid range of size and with other properties to be reviewed here. The processes by which the units arise are exceedingly simple. In the laboratory, we usually dissolve the synthetic polymer in hot aqueous solution, boil the solution for 10 seconds, decant the hot clear supernatant liquid, and allow it to cool. . . .

The numbers of proteinoid microspheres produced are immense. One gram of polymer will yield, for example, ten billion units. When one views the experiments in the context of the natural scenario and bears in mind that while close to uniform the units are variable, he can see the opportunity for numerous natural experimental variations within each natural experiment. . . .

The relative uniformity of size of the particles permits quantitative experiments. Such experiments have shown that the microspheres swell or shrink when transferred to solutions which are, respectively, more hypotonic or hypertonic than those in which they were made.

In 1924, Stearn and Stearn attributed the Gram-stainability of bacteria to the protein content of the organisms. Accordingly, the possibility that the microspheres made, in turn, from material closely resembling protein invited attention. The microspheres were indeed found to accept the Gram stain. . . .

In Fig. 6 is a clearer picture of the simulation of cell division. These units are in the 10-20μ range of size. Several biologists have asked if these are not actually dividing bacteria which contaminate the field being viewed. They are not, inasmuch as they are produced from hot aqueous solutions within minutes and can be redissolved by warming, again to deposit micron-sized spherules. Another question is that of whether the sequence represented constitutes fusion or fission.

Time-lapse studies indicate that the process in these experiments is indeed fission. . . . A septate kind of fission is modeled. Other sequences show complete separation. These pictures are also some of the evidence that the boundary is membranous in having a primitive kind of selectivity. The polymer in the interior diffuses out through the boundary with the raised pH, without dissipation of the boundary itself. As yet, no compositional difference has been found between the washed boundaries and the solid of the original microspheres.

The microspheres are capable of bringing about changes in other materials as well as in themselves. The ability to split glucose, such as observed in the proteinoid of which they are made, is found also in suspensions of microspheres made from these polymers, albeit at a moderately reduced level. The known ability of zinc salts to split ATP has been incorporated into the units by bonding zinc in them in a suitable way. These particles then exhibit some interesting dynamic properties.

The stability of the proteinoid microspheres has permitted a submicroscopic view of some of their structural features. . . .

Most of the material looks like the granular cytoplasm of the bacterium. A suggestion of a boundary can be made out in this picture. . . .

[Where] the process has proceeded further, [there] can be observed a feature which was entirely unexpected before it appeared — the double layer. The double layer has long been studied as a unique aspect of true cells. Until the recent studies of Green and associates, this bilamellar structure was believed to require phospholipid, but Green has identified a "structural protein" in mitochondria.

The results pictured thus illustrate that the self-organizing properties of macromolecules can manifest themselves in a manner that yields units that simulate many of the properties of true cells and which may also have contributed significantly to the sucession of phenomena producing cells. . . .

Evolution: Process and Product

During the eighteenth and nineteenth centuries man's knowledge of his world expanded into the past with the discovery of fossils and into the present by increased world-wide exploration. Both forces increased man's awareness not only of the tremendous diversity of life but also of the oftentimes striking similarities and distributional patterns of organisms. The tangible evidence from the fossil record demonstrated an immensity of time as well as the phenomenon of change as a characteristic of organisms. The fossil record constituted a mounting body of evidence, often referred to as the "fact of evolution" by those who denied each organism its special creation by a supreme being. Confrontation with morphological similarities too striking to be deigned as capricious suggested that organisms undergo an orderly, fathomable process of evolving (literally, unfolding) and that there has been a progression of organic forms over eons of time.

In characteristic fashion, a number of scientists proposed various rational, although largely speculative, schemes and mechanisms to explain these phenomena. Lamarck's purposeful mechanisms, proposed at the beginning of the nineteenth century (p. 153), carried considerable influence well into the twentieth century; in no small measure this may have been successful because of their teleological explanation. But the high point of evolutionary theory came in the thinking of Charles Darwin (p. 157) and Alfred Russel Wallace (p. 161) in the middle of the nineteenth century. To even the casual observer of scientific history, the independent but simultaneous convergence of Darwin and Wallace on the importance of natural selection as an evolutionary mechanism is a phenomenon worthy of its unique place in the annals of human thought.

The post-Darwin period was one of some grandiloquence and often unsoundly based speculation. It led also to much generalization and overgeneralization. Among examples of the latter may be cited Häckel's dictum that "ontogeny recapitulates phylogeny" (p. 165). This was a generally well-based attempt to show an alternate line of evidence for the evolutionary process, but it extended far beyond the confirming evidence then, or now.

The first extensive analysis of the role of geographic isolation in evolution came in studies by Henry Crampton in 1917 on the snails of Tahiti (p. 174). Raymond Dart's discovery of the man-ape *Australopithecus* in 1925 (p. 178) provided one of the essential "missing links" in unfolding the story of human evolution. Among the most recent confirmations of "evolution in action" have been studies on melanism in moths (Kettlewell, p. 190).

The mechanisms of evolution proposed by Darwin and Wallace have undergone continued refinement and modification in the intervening period. The major augmentation has come from genetics, particularly in the concept of gene pools and shifts in gene frequencies. Hugo de Vries, in 1909, proposed that mutation constituted the source of variation (p. 170). In 1908, Hardy provided a mathematical model for determining gene frequencies based on mendelian principles (p. 168). Disruption of the equilibrium in gene freqencies results in adaptive or nonadaptive change found in the population. One of the ways in which the equilibrium can be changed has been discussed by Sewall Wright (p. 186). Dobzhansky and others have shown that selection does occur under natural conditions and can be recognized at the level of the chromosome (p. 182).

42

of the influence of the environment on the activities and habits of animals, and the influence of the activities and habits of these living bodies in modifying their organisation and structure

JEAN BAPTISTE de LAMARCK

We are not here concerned with an argument, but with the examination of a positive fact — a fact which is of more general application than is supposed, and which has not received the attention that it deserves, no doubt because it is usually very difficult to recognize. This fact consists in the influence that is exerted by the environment on the various living bodies exposed to it. . . .

I must now explain what I mean by this statement: *the environment affects the shape and organisation of animals,* that is to say that when the environment becomes very different, it produces in course of time corresponding modifications in the shape and organisation of animals.

It is true if this statement were to be taken literally, I should be convicted of an error; for, whatever the environment may do, it does not work any direct modification whatever in the shape and organisation of animals.

But great alterations in the environment of animals lead to great alterations in their needs, and these alterations in their needs necessarily lead to others in their activities. Now if the new needs become permanent, the animals then adopt new habits which last as long as the needs that evoked them. This is easy to demonstrate, and indeed requires no amplification. . . .

Thus to obtain a knowledge of the true causes of that great diversity of shapes and habits found in the various known animals, we must

Reprinted with the publisher's permission from the translation by Hugh Elliot of Chapter 7 of Zoological philosophy (1809), The Macmillan Co., London (1914).

reflect that the infinitely diversified but slowly changing environment in which the animals of each race have successively been placed has involved each of them in new needs and corresponding alterations in their habits. This is a truth which, once recognised, cannot be disputed. Now we shall easily discern how the new needs may have been satisfied, and the new habits acquired, if we pay attention to the two following laws of nature, which are always verified by observation.

First Law

In every animal which has not passed the limit of its development, a more frequent and continuous use of any organ gradually strengthens, develops, and enlarges that organ, and gives it a power proportional to the length of time it has been so used; while the permanent disuse of any organ imperceptibly weakens and deteriorates it, and progressively diminishes its functional capacity, until it finally disappears.

Second Law

All the acquisitions or losses wrought by nature on individuals, through the influence of the environment in which their race has long been placed, and hence through the influence of the predominant use or permanent disuse of any organ; all these are preserved by reproduction to the new individuals which arise, provided that the acquired modifications are common to both sexes, or at least to the individuals which produce the young.

Here we have two permanent truths, which can only be doubted by those who have never observed or followed the operations of nature, or by those who have allowed themselves to be drawn into the error which I shall now proceed to combat. . . .

Now I am going to prove that the permanent disuse of any organ first decreases its functional capacity, and then gradually reduces the organ and causes it to disappear or even become extinct, if this disuse lasts for a very long period throughout successive generations of animals of the same race. . . .

Since such a proposition could only be accepted on proof, and not on mere authority, let us endeavour to make it clear by citing the chief known facts which substantiate it. . . .

Eyes in the head are characteristic of a great number of different animals, and essentially constitute a part of the plan of organisation of the vertebrates.

Yet the mole, whose habits require a very small use of sight, has only minute and hardly visible eyes, because it uses that organ so little.

Olivier's *Spalax* (*Voyage en Égypte et en Perse*), which lives underground like the mole, and is apparently exposed to daylight even less than the mole, has altogether lost the use of sight: so that it shows nothing more than vestiges of this organ. Even these vestiges are entirely hidden under the skin and other parts, which cover them up and do not leave the slightest access to light.

The *Proteus,* an aquatic reptile allied to the salamanders and living in deep dark caves under the water, has, like the *Spalax,* only vestiges of the organ of sight, vestiges which are covered up and hidden in the same way.

The following consideration is decisive on the question which I am now discussing.

Light does not penetrate everywhere; consequently animals which habitually live in places where it does not penetrate have no opportunity of exercising their organ of sight, if nature has endowed them with one. Now animals belonging to a plan of organisation of which eyes were a necessary part must have originally had them. Since, however, there are found among them some which have lost the use of this organ and which show nothing more than hidden and covered-up vestiges of them, it becomes clear that the shrinkage and even disappearance of the organ in question are the results of a permanent disuse of that organ. . . .

We have seen that the disuse of any organ modifies, reduces and finally extinguishes it. I shall now prove that the constant use of any organ, accompanied by efforts to get the most out of it, strengthens and enlarges that organ, or creates new ones to carry on functions that have become necessary.

The bird which is drawn to the water by its need of finding there the prey on which it lives separates the digits of its feet in trying to strike the water and move about on the surface. The skin which unites these digits at their base acquires the habit of being stretched by these continually repeated separations of the digits; thus in course of time there are formed large webs which unite the digits of ducks, geese, etc., as we actually find them. In the same way efforts to swim, that is to push against the water so as to move about in it, have stretched the membranes between the digits of frogs, sea tortoises, the otter, beaver, etc.

On the other hand, a bird which is accustomed to perch on trees and which springs from individuals all of whom had acquired this habit necessarily has longer digits on its feet and differently shaped from those of the aquatic animals that I have just named. Its claws in time become lengthened, sharpened and curved into hooks, to clasp the branches on which the animal so often rests. . . .

Everything then combines to prove my statement, namely: that it is not the shape either of the body or its parts which gives rise to the habits of animals and their mode of life; but that it is, on the contrary, the habits, mode of life and all the other influences of the environment which have in course of time built up the shape of the body and of the parts of animals. With new shapes, new faculties have been acquired, and little by little nature has succeeded in fashioning animals such as we actually see them. . . .

43

on the variation of organic beings in a state of nature; on the natural means of selection; on the comparison of domestic races and true species

CHARLES DARWIN

De Candolle, in an eloquent passage, has declared that all nature is at war, one organism with another, or with external nature. Seeing the contented face of nature, this may at first well be doubted; but reflection will inevitably prove it to be true. The war, however, is not constant, but recurrent in a slight degree at short periods, and more severely at occasional more distant periods; and hence its effects are easily overlooked. It is the doctrine of Malthus applied in most cases with tenfold force. As in every climate there are seasons, for each of its inhabitants, of greater and less abundance, so all annually breed; and the moral restraint which in some small degree checks the increase of mankind is entirely lost. Even slow-breeding mankind has doubled in twenty-five years; and if he could increase his food with greater ease, he would double in less time. But for animals without artificial means, the amount of food for each species must, *on an average*, be constant, whereas the increase of all organisms tends to be geometrical, and in a vast majority of cases at an enormous ratio. Suppose in a certain spot there are eight pairs of birds, and that *only* four pairs of them annually (including double hatches) rear only four young, and that these go on rearing their young at the same rate, then at the end of seven years (a short life, excluding violent deaths, for any bird) there will be 2048 birds, instead of the original sixteen. As this increase is quite impossible,

Reprinted from the Journal of the Proceedings of the Linnaean Society of London, Vol. 3 (1859), pp. 45-62. This extract from an unpublished work by Darwin and the following selection by Wallace were read before the Linnaean Society July 1, 1858, by Charles Lyell and Joseph Hooker.

we must conclude either that birds do not rear nearly half their young, or that the average life of a bird is, from accident, not nearly seven years. Both checks probably concur. The same kind of calculation applied to all plants and animals affords results more or less striking, but in very few instances more striking than in man.

Many practical illustrations of this rapid tendency to increase are on record, among which, during peculiar seasons, are the extraordinary numbers of certain animals. . . . Reflect on the enormous multiplying power *inherent and annually in action* in all animals; reflect on the countless seeds scattered by a hundred ingenious contrivances, year after year, over the whole face of the land; and yet we have every reason to suppose that the average percentage of each of the inhabitants of a country usually remains constant. Finally, let it be borne in mind that this average number of individuals (the external conditions remaining the same) in each country is kept up by recurrent struggles against other species or against external nature (as on the borders of the Arctic regions, where the cold checks life), and that ordinarily each individual of every species holds its place, either by its own struggle and capacity of acquiring nourishment in some period of its life, from the egg upwards; or by the struggle of its parents (in short-lived organisms, when the main check occurs at longer intervals) with other individuals of the *same* or *different* species.

But let the external conditions of a country alter. If in a small degree, the relative proportions of the inhabitants will in most cases simply be slightly changed; but let the number of inhabitants be small, as on an island, and free access to it from other countries be circumscribed, and let the change of conditions continue progressing (forming new stations), in such a case the original inhabitants must cease to be as perfectly adapted to the changed conditions as they were originally. It has been shown in a former part of this work, that such changes of external conditions would, from their acting on the reproductive system, probably cause the organization of those beings which were most affected to become, as under domestication, plastic. Now, can it be doubted, from the struggle each individual has to obtain subsistence, that any minute variation in structure, habits, or instincts, adapting that individual better to the new conditions, would tell upon its vigour and health? In the struggle it would have a better *chance* of surviving; and those of its offspring which inherited the variation, be it ever so slight, would also have a better *chance*. Yearly more are bred than can survive; the smallest grain in the balance, in the long run, must tell on which death shall fall, and which shall survive. Let this work of selection on the one hand, and death on the other, go on for a thousand generations, who will pretend to affirm that it would produce no effect, when we remember what, in a few years, Bakewell effected in cattle, and Western in sheep, by this identical principle of selection?

To give an imaginary example from changes in progress on an island: — let the organization of a canine animal which preyed chiefly on rabbits, but sometimes on hares, become slightly plastic; let these same changes cause the number of rabbits very slowly to decrease, and the number of hares to increase; the effect of this would be that the fox or dog would be driven to try to catch more hares; his organization, however, being slightly plastic, those individuals with the lightest forms, longest limbs, and best eyesight, let the difference be ever so small, would be slightly favoured, and would tend to live longer, and to survive during that time of the year when food was scarcest; they would also rear more young, which would tend to inherit these slight peculiarities. The less fleet ones would be rigidly destroyed. I can see no more reason to doubt that these causes in a thousand generations would produce a marked effect, and adapt the form of the fox or dog to the catching of hares instead of rabbits, than that greyhounds can be improved by selection and careful breeding. So would it be with plants under similar circumstances. If the number of individuals of a species with plumed seeds could be increased by greater powers of dissemination within its own area (that is, if the check to increase fell chiefly on the seeds), those seeds which were provided with ever so little more down, would in the long run be most disseminated; hence a greater number of seeds thus formed would germinate, and would tend to produce plants inheriting the slightly better-adapted down.

Besides this natural means of selection, by which those individuals are preserved, whether in their egg, or larval, or mature state, which are best adapted to the place they fill in nature, there is a second agency at work in most unisexual animals tending to produce the same effect, namely, the struggle of the males for the females. These struggles are generally decided by the law of battle, but in the case of birds, apparently, by the charms of their song, by their beauty or their power of courtship, as in the dancing rock-thrush of Guiana. The most vigorous and healthy males, implying perfect adaptation, must generally gain the victory in their contests. This kind of selection, however, is less rigorous than the other; it does not require the death of the less successful, but gives to them fewer descendants. The struggle falls, moreover, at a time of year when food is generally abundant, and perhaps the effect chiefly produced would be the modification of the secondary sexual characters, which are not related to the power of obtaining food, or to defence from enemies, but to fighting with or rivalling other males.

The result of this struggle amongst the males may be compared in some respects to that produced by those agriculturists who pay less attention to the careful selection of all their young animals, and more to the occasional use of a choice mate.

44

on the tendency of varieties to depart indefinitely from the original type

ALFRED RUSSEL WALLACE

One of the strongest arguments which have been adduced to prove the original and permanent distinctness of species is that *varieties* produced in a state of domesticity are more or less unstable, and often have a tendency, if left to themselves, to return to the normal form of the parent species; and this instability is considered to be a distinctive peculiarity of all varieties, even of those occurring among wild animals in a state of nature, and to constitute a provision for preserving unchanged the originally created distinct species. . . .

It will be observed that this argument rests entirely on the assumption, that *varieties* occurring in a state of nature are in all respects analogous to or even identical with those of domestic animals, and are governed by the same laws as regards their permanence or further variation. But it is the object of the present paper to show that this assumption is altogether false, that there is a general principle in nature which will cause many *varieties* to survive the parent species, and to give rise to successive variations departing further and further from the original type, and which also produces, in domesticated animals, the tendency of varieties to return to the parent form.

The life of wild animals is a struggle for existence. The full exertion of all their faculties and all their energies is required to preserve their own existence and provide for that of their infant offspring. The possibility of procuring food during the least favourable seasons and of

Reprinted from the Journal of the Proceedings of the Linnaean Society of London, Vol. 3 (1859), pp. 45-62. See note at beginning of Darwin's paper (p. 157).

escaping the attacks of their most dangerous enemies are the primary conditions which determine the existence both of individuals and of entire species. These conditions will also determine the population of a species; and by a careful consideration of all the circumstances we may be enabled to comprehend, and in some degree to explain, what at first sight appears so inexplicable – the excessive abundance of some species, while others closely allied to them are very rare. . . .

It appears evident, therefore, that so long as a country remains physically unchanged, the numbers of its animal population cannot materially increase. If one species does so, some others requiring the same kind of food must diminish in proportion. The numbers that die annually must be immense; and as the individual existence of each animal depends upon itself, those that die must be the weakest – the very young, the aged, and the diseased – while those that prolong their existence can only be the most perfect in health and vigour – those who are best able to obtain food regularly, and avoid their numerous enemies. It is, as we commenced by remarking, "a struggle for existence," in which the weakest and least perfectly organized must always succumb.

Now it is clear that what takes place among the individuals of a species must also occur among the several allied species of a group – viz. that those which are best adapted to obtain a regular supply of food, and to defend themselves against the attacks of their enemies and the vicissitudes of the seasons, must necessarily obtain and preserve a superiority in population; while those species which from some defect of power or organization are the least capable of counteracting the vicissitudes of food, supply, &c., must diminish in numbers, and, in extreme cases, become altogether extinct. Between these extremes the species will present various degrees of capacity for ensuring the means of preserving life; and it is thus we account for the abundance or rarity of species. Our ignorance will generally prevent us from accurately tracing the effects to their causes; but could we become perfectly acquainted with the organization and habits of the various species of animals, and could we measure the capacity of each for performing the different acts necessary to its safety and existence under all the varying circumstances by which it is surrounded, we might be able even to calculate the proportionate abundance of individuals which is the necessary result.

If now we have succeeded in establishing these two points – 1st, *that the animal population of a country is generally stationary, being kept down by a periodical deficiency of food, and other checks;* and 2nd, *that the comparative abundance or scarcity of the individuals of the several species is entirely due to their organization and resulting habits, which, rendering it more difficult to procure a regular supply of food and to provide for their personal safety in some cases than in others, can only be balanced by a difference in the population which have to exist in a given area* – we shall be in a condition to proceed to the consideration of *varieties,* to which the preceding remarks have a direct and very important application.

Most or perhaps all the variations from the typical form of a species must have some definite effect, however slight, on the habits or capacities of the individuals. Even a change of colour might, by rendering them more or less distinguishable, affect their safety; a greater or less development of hair might modify their habits. More important changes, such as an increase in the power or dimensions of the limbs or any of the external organs, would more or less affect their mode of procuring food or the range of country which they inhabit. It is also evident that most changes would affect, either favourably or adversely, the powers of prolonging existence. An antelope with shorter or weaker legs must necessarily suffer more from the attacks of the feline carnivora; the passenger pigeon with less powerful wings would sooner or later be affected in its powers of procuring a regular supply of food; and in both cases the result must necessarily be a diminution of the population of the modified species. If, on the other hand, any species should produce a variety having slightly increased powers of preserving existence, that variety must inevitably in time acquire a superiority in numbers. These results must follow as surely as old age, intemperance, or scarcity of food produce an increased mortality. In both cases there may be many individual exceptions; but on the average the rule will invariably be found to hold good. All varieties will therefore fall into two classes – those which under the same conditions would never reach the population of the parent species, and those which would in time obtain and keep a numerical superiority. Now, let some alteration of physical conditions occur in the district – a long period of drought, a destruction of vegetation by locusts, the irruption of some new carnivorous animal seeking "pastures new" – any change in fact tending to render existence more difficult to the species in question, and tasking its utmost powers to avoid complete extermination; it is evident that, of all the individuals composing the species, those forming the least numerous and most feebly organized variety would suffer first, and, were the pressure severe, must soon become extinct. The same causes continuing in action, the parent species would next suffer, would gradually diminish in numbers, and with a recurrence of similar unfavourable conditions might also become extinct. The superior variety would then alone remain, and on a return to favourable circumstances would rapidly increase in numbers and occupy the place of the extinct species and variety.

The *variety* would now have replaced the *species,* of which it would be a more perfectly developed and more highly organized form. It would be in all respects better adapted to secure its safety and to prolong its individual existence and that of the race. Such a variety *could not* return to the original form; for that form is an inferior one, and could never compete with it for existence. Granted, therefore, a "tendency" to reproduce the original type of the species, still the variety must ever remain preponderant in numbers, and under adverse physical conditions *again alone survive.* But this new, improved, and populous race might itself, in course of time, give rise to new varieties, exhibiting several diverging modifications of form, any of which, tending to increase the facilities for preserving existence, must, by the same general law, in their turn become predominant. Here, then, we have *progression and continued divergence* deduced from the general laws which regulate the existence of animals in a state of nature, and from the undisputed fact that varieties do frequently occur. . . .

45

the evolution of man

ERNST HACKEL

. . . These two divisions of our science, ontogeny, or the history of the germ, phylogeny, or the history of the tribe, are most intimately connected, and the one cannot be understood without the other. The close intertwining of both branches, the increased proportions which germ history and tribal history lend to each other, alone raise biogeny (or the history of organic evolution, in the widest sense) to the rank of a philosophic natural science. The connection between the two is not external and superficial, but deeply internal and causal. Our knowledge of this connection has been but very recently obtained; it is most clearly and accurately expressed in the comprehensive statement which I call "*the fundamental law of organic evolution*," or more briefly, "*the first principle of biogeny.*"

This fundamental law, to which we shall recur again and again, and on the recognition of which depends the thorough understanding of the history of evolution, is briefly expressed in the proposition: that the history of the germ is an epitome of the history of the descent; or, in other words: that ontogeny is a recapitulation of phylogeny; or, somewhat more explicitly: that the series of forms through which the individual organism passes during its progress from the egg cell to its fully developed state, is a brief, compressed reproduction of the long series of forms through which the animal ancestors of that organism (or the

Reprinted from the translation (translator unknown) published by Appleton and Co., New York (1879).

ancestral forms of its species) have passed from the earliest periods of so-called organic creation down to the present time.

The causal nature of the relation which connects the history of the germ (embryology, or ontogeny) with that of the tribe (phylogeny) is dependent on the phenomena of heredity and adaptation. When these are properly understood, and their fundamental importance in determining the forms of organisms recognized, we may go a step further, and say: Phylogenesis is the mechanical cause of ontogenesis. The evolution of the tribe which is dependent on the laws of heredity and adaptation, effects all the events which take place in the course of the evolution of the germ or embryo.

The chain of different animal forms which, according to the theory of descent, constitutes the series of ancestors, or chain of forefathers of every higher organism, and hence also of man, always forms a connected whole. This unbroken succession of forms may be represented by the letters of the alphabet A, B, C, D, E, etc., down to Z, in their alphabetical order. In apparent contradiction to this, the history of the individual evolution or the ontogeny of most organisms show us only a fragment of this series of forms, so that the interrupted chain of embryonic forms would be represented by something like: A, B, F, H, I, K, L, etc.; or, in other cases, thus: B, D, H, L, M, N, etc. Several evolutionary forms have, therefore, usually dropped out of the originally unbroken chain of forms. In many cases also (retaining the figure of the repeated alphabet) one or more letters representing ancestral forms, are replaced in the corresponding places among the embryonic forms by equivalent letters of another alphabet. Thus, for example, in place of the Latin B or D, a Greek β or Δ is often found. Here, therefore, the text of the biogenetic first principle is vitiated, while in the former case it was epitomized. This gives more importance to the fact that, notwithstanding this, the sequence remains the same, so that we are enabled to recognize its original order.

Indeed, there is always a complete parallelism between the two series of evolution. This is, however, vitiated by the fact that in most cases many forms which formerly existed and actually lived in the phylogenetic series are now wanting, and have been lost from the ontogenetic series of evolution. If the parallelism between the two series were perfect, and if this great fundamental law of the causal connection between ontogeny and phylogeny, in the strict sense of the word, had full and unconditional sway, we should only have to ascertain, with the aid of microscope and scalpel, the series of forms through which the fertilized human egg passes before it attains its complete development. Such an examination would at once give us a complete picture of the remarkable series of forms through which the animal ancestors of the human race have passed, from the beginning of organic creation to the first appearance of man. But this reproduction of the phylogeny in the ontogeny is complete only in rare instances, and seldom corresponds to the entire series of the letters of the alphabet. In fact, in most cases the epitome is very incomplete, and greatly altered and perverted by causes which we shall investigate hereafter. Hence we are seldom able to determine directly, by means of its ontogeny, the different forms through which the ancestry of each organism has passed; on the contrary, we commonly find – and not less so in the phylogeny of man – a number of gaps. We are, however, able to bridge over the greater part of these gaps satisfactorily by the help of comparative anatomy, though not to fill them up directly by ontogenetic research. It is therefore all the more important that we are acquainted with a considerable number of lower animal forms which still find place in the history of the individual evolution of man. In such cases, from the nature of the transient individual form, we may quite safely infer the nature of the ancestral animal form. . . .

46

mendelian proportions in a mixed population

G. H. HARDY

I am reluctant to intrude in a discussion concerning matters of which I have no expert knowledge, and I should have expected the very simple point which I wish to make to have been familiar to biologists. However, some remarks of Mr. Udny Yule, to which Mr. R. C. Punnett has called my attention, suggest that it may still be worth making.

In the *Proceedings of the Royal Society of Medicine* Mr. Yule is reported to have suggested, as a criticism of the Mendelian position, that if brachydactyly is dominant "in the course of time one would expect, in the absence of counteracting factors, to get three brachydactylous persons to one normal."

It is not difficult to prove, however, that such an expectation would be quite groundless. Suppose that *Aa* is a pair of Mendelian characters, A being dominant, and that in any given generation the numbers of pure dominants *(AA)*, heterozygotes (*Aa*), and pure recessives (*aa*) are as $p : 2q : r$. Finally, suppose that the numbers are fairly large, so that the mating may be regarded as random, that the sexes are evenly distributed among the three varieties, and that all are equally fertile. A little mathematics of the multiplication-table type is enough to show that in the next generation the numbers will be as

$$(p + q)^2 : 2(p + q)\ (q + r) : (q + r)^2,$$

or as $p_1 : 2q_1 : r_1$, say.

Reprinted from Science, Vol. 28 (1908), pp. 49-50.

The interesting question is – in what circumstances will this distribution be the same as that in the generation before? It is easy to see that the condition for this is $q^2 = pr$. And since $q_1^2 = p_1r_1$, whatever the values of p, q and r may be, the distribution will in any case continue unchanged after the second generation.

Suppose, to take a definite instance, that A is brachydactyly, and that we start from a population of pure brachydactylous and pure normal persons, say in the ratio of 1:10,000. Then $p = 1$, $q = 0$, $r = 10{,}000$ and $p_1 = 1$, $q_1 = 10{,}000$, $r_1 = 100{,}000{,}000$. If brachydactyly is dominant, the proportion of brachydactylous persons in the second generation is 20,001 : 100,020,001, or practically 2 : 10,000, twice that in the first generation; and this proportion will afterwards have no tendency whatever to increase. If, on the other hand brachydactyly were recessive, the proportion in the second generation would be 1 : 100,020,001, or practically 1 : 100,000,000, and this proportion would afterwards have no tendency to decrease.

In a word, there is not the slightest foundation for the idea that a dominant character should show a tendency to spread over a whole population, or that a recessive should tend to die out.

I ought perhaps to add a few words on the effect of the small deviations from the theoretical proportions which will, of course, occur in every generation. Such a distribution as $p_1 : 2q_1 : r_1$, which satisfies the condition $q_1^2 = p_1r_1$, we may call a *stable* distribution. In actual fact we shall obtain in the second generation not $p_1 : 2q_1 : r_1$ but a slightly different distribution $p_1' : 2q_1' : r_1'$, which is not "stable." This should, according to theory, give us in the third generation a "stable" distribution $p_2 : 2q_2 : r_2$, also differing slightly from $p_1 : 2q_1 : r_1$; and so on. The sense in which the distribution $p_1 : 2q_1 : r_1$ is "stable" is this, that if we allow for the effect of casual deviations in any subsequent generation, we should, according to theory, obtain at the next generation a new "stable" distribution differing but slightly from the original distribution.

I have, of course, considered only the very simplest hypotheses possible. Hypotheses other than that of purely random mating will give different results, and, of course, if, as appears to be the case sometimes, the character is not independent of that of sex, or has an influence on fertility, the whole question may be greatly complicated. But such complications seem to be irrelevant to the simple issue raised by Mr. Yule's remarks.

P. S. I understand from Mr. Punnett that he has submitted the substance of what I have said above to Mr. Yule, and that the latter would accept it as a satisfactory answer to the difficulty that he raised. The "stability" of the particular ratio 1 : 2 : 1 is recognized by Professor Karl Pearson.

47

the origin of species by mutation

HUGO de VRIES

We saw in the second chapter that species cannot have originated by the natural selection of the extreme variants afforded by fluctuating variability.

We have therefore now to show that the observations which have been made on this subject can be simply and completely explained on the hypothesis of sudden changes. When such transformations occur among cultivated plants – and they often do – they are called spontaneous or, as Darwin called them, *single variations* moreover they are almost always inherited, if not in their entirety, at any rate to a very considerable extent.

We may express therefore the essence of the mutation theory in the words: "*Species have arisen after the manner of so-called spontaneous variations.*" And in our critical survey of the facts we therefore have to consider how far the information at our disposal justifies this view. . . .

It is the actual theory of descent itself that would profit most by a proper appreciation of the conception of species. This theory which is recognized in morphology, embryology, in systematic work and in comparative anatomy as the guiding principle of all speculation and inquiry has remained almost without influence on experimental biology. At first it raised the hope that science would succeed not only in discovering the common origin of all species but in bringing the origin of

Reprinted from The mutation theory (Vol. 1), translated by J. B. Farmer and A. D. Darbishire, Open Court Publishing Co., Chicago (1909).

species within the range of direct observation and even in placing in our hands a certain amount of control over these natural processes.

But we are today just as far from this goal as we were in Darwin's time. The opponents of the theory of descent have from the very beginning argued that we ought at least to be able to observe the origin of species and, perhaps, even to effect it experimentally. This criticism must even now be recognized as fully justified, although it is of course no longer one on the answer to which the validity of the doctrine of descent depends. . . .

The object of an experimental treatment of these phenomena must assuredly be to make the origin of the units which really exist in nature the subject of experiment and observation. We must deal not with the origin of the groups made by the systematist but with those which are presented by nature.

There is no question that these elementary species often do arise in the garden and in agricultural practice. But in the first place they are only noticed when they have become established and when therefore the chance of observing the mode of their origin is irrevocably lost. And in the second place we smooth the matter over by calling the new forms "Varieties." . . .

Such varieties are just as distinct and just as constant in cultivation as the best species. If it is still considered proper that they should be called varieties, then it follows that varieties are nothing less than a particular form of species. *Varieties are only small species,* as Darwin has said. . . .

The reader is now in a position to understand what I mean when I say that our business is not really with the origin of species but with the development of specific characters.

The diversity of organic forms is due to the existence of a vast number of differentiating characters. And the question we have to answer is, "How have these characters arisen?"

Subspecies become species by extinction of intermediate forms. New species can arise by crossing when the peculiarities of two forms already existing are united to form a single new one; and so on. But these are not cases of the origin of specific characters. Many species and even genera and still larger systematic groups have arisen by these characters disappearing or becoming latent. The origin of the monocotyledons from the dicotyledons is regarded by some as coming under this head (Delpino). But loss and latency are obviously special cases which do not directly touch the main question of progress in the animal and vegetable kingdom.

The question is not how many characters peculiar to itself must an animal or plant possess to justify its elevation to specific rank, but: how have these characters arisen, or how can they arise?

In other words: the mutation and the actual process of mutating must become the object of investigation. And if we once discover the nature of this process, not only will our insight into the actual relationship of living organisms become much deeper, but we may even hope that we may be able to gain some measure of control over the formation of species. If the breeder has obtained control over variability, why should he not obtain it over mutation as well?

It is clear that we can only advance by very small steps dealing at each step with a single mutation. But even single mutations may be of enormous importance in horticulture or agriculture. Much that now seems unattainable may come within our power if only we can obtain some insight into the fundamental principles involved in mutation. There lies here a wide field of work the results of which will be as important to the biologist as to the practical man. . . .

According to the theory of selection the origin of a new form is a gradual process which we can observe whilst it is taking place. But the evidence at our disposal does not support this theory. It is true that forms which have arisen suddenly exhibit a high degree of fluctuating variability and so give the selector the opportunity of intensifying the new character. But that is a very different matter from the gradual origin of the new character. . . .

The chief merit of Darwin's theory of selection was that it explained the adaptation which is seen on all hands in organic nature on purely natural principles and without the aid of any teleological conception. It is because it does this so completely that the theory of descent has gained such universal acceptance. The universal belief in the kinship of living forms in its turn now makes the experimental study of the manner in which one species arises from another possible. Nay, it challenges us to such an inquiry. How the species which exist at the present time arose in the past is evidently a historical question which can only be directly answered in a very few cases. But the determination of the mode of origin of species must soon become the subject of inquiry just like any other physiological process.

According to the Darwinian principle, species-forming variability — mutability — does not take place in definite directions. According to that theory, deviations take place in almost every direction without preference for any particular one, and especially without preference for that direction along which differentiation happens to be proceeding.

Every hypothesis which differs from Darwin's in this respect must be rejected as teleological and unscientific.

The struggle for existence chooses from among the mutations at its disposal those which are the best adapted at the moment; in this way alone can their survival be explained. . . .

48

problem of a factorial environment

HENRY E. CRAMPTON

A just estimate of the relative values of congenital and environmental factors of organic constitution is still one of the principal aims of biology today, as it has been for many centuries. The whole problem involves two matters, first, the question as to how much of an individual's make-up may be due to the incidence of external influences, and, second, the question as to the transfer to offspring of environmental effects if such, indeed, are actually induced. The brilliant investigations of recent decades in experimental genetics, cytology and embryology warrant the broad general statement that congenital factors are paramount, that they are solely responsible for qualities as such, and that if external influences exert any effects whatever their role is limited to quantitative modifications of the expression of innate qualities, which modifications fail to reappear in offspring.

The present study deals with species and varieties in a state of nature and with the differences displayed by the snails down to the unitary items of individual diversity. Its category, therefore, is sharply contrasted with that of experimental studies in the laboratory and garden, although the two have the common element of an interest in the initial episodes of organic differentiation. The results of my own studies accord fully with those of experimental genetics, as I understand them to be capable of formulation in the above-stated terms. Almost every chapter includes some discussion of the problem of environment, so it remains

Reprinted with the publisher's permission from The variation, distribution and evolution of the genus Partula. The Carnegie Institution of Washington Publication 228 (1916), pp. 1-311.

only to survey the material in a general way, with some regard to the whole distribution of the species of *Partula* throughout Oceania, and with more special consideration of the forms dwelling in Moorea.

Each archipelago of Oceania in which "high" islands of volcanic nature occur possesses endemic species that are distinguished by lesser or greater degrees of individuality in their several characters. Few would contend today, I believe, that environmental conditions peculiar to the group are responsible for the occurrence of *Partula gibba, Partula radiolata, Partula fragilis* and *Partula salifana* in the Mariana Islands only, and that the complex of species existing in the Society Islands differs because the diverse organic qualities of the snails have been evoked by surrounding circumstances which are not the same in the Society Islands as in the Mariana Islands. The biological nature of the organisms and their relations to the various ecological conditions of their settings leave no doubt that congenital factors only are responsible for the contrasts displayed by the two groups of endemic species specified.

Moorea possesses its own indigenous forms which do not exist in Tahiti or in another island of the Society Group. Only an appeal to ignorance could be made in an endeavor to account for the distinctions of the Moorean species by reference to external causation, for all efforts are futile to discover an inorganic or heterogeneric biological difference between Moorea and Tahiti. Through their proximity and similar geological origin, Tahiti and Moorea are virtually as much alike as are the two subdivisions of the former island.

Narrowing the further discussion to the forms of Moorea, the first point is that the same general principle of geographical distribution holds for the insular complex as for the island groups in their relation to the array of the whole archipelago; in general terms, the formula is that an essential correlation exists between the degree of likeness on the part of the organisms and the degree of geographical proximity or isolation of their habitats. The species *Partula olympia* is more nearly related to *Partula mooreana* of the same island than it is to any species of another island. The similarity in question is fully accounted for by the origin of the two species from a common ancestral stock, and the distinctions must be viewed as the products of divergent congenital differentiation. There is no need for an appeal to unknown insular circumstances of identical nature which might have called into being the qualities of likeness and which are sufficiently different in detail in Mouaputa Valley and in the Vaianai region to bring about such distinctions as are displayed by the two species. The same argument holds for the other pairs of related species which inhabit separate regions of Moorea, namely *Partula suturalis* and *Partula dendroica, Partula aurantia* and *Partula mirabilis.*

Considering next those species which dwell in sharply restricted territories, we find it impossible to discover environmental factors which would account for the appearance of *Partula solitaria* only in a subsidiary division of Faatoai Valley, of *Partula tohiveana* in Fareaito Valley alone, and of *Partula olympia* in Mouaputa Valley and nowhere else, especially when *Partula tæniata* exists in association with all of these forms as one and the same species. Obviously it would be inconsistent to attribute the like qualities of the members of *Partula tæniata* to supposedly similar circumstances throughout the island and at the same time to refer the distinctions of the other species to diverse external conditions. Other species inhabit wider areas than the three specified above, but in no case can the likenesses displayed by the colonial components of any one of them be referred to elements of the environment peculiar to a particular sector or area. The species *Partula aurantia, Partula mirabilis* and *Partula mooreana* are especially significant because trustworthy evidence shows that each of these species has expanded its territory in recent years without any departure from its specific distinctions in the new-won areas. *Partula suturalis* contributes many items of additional proof, presenting as it does two differentiated varieties which occupy separate but contiguous regions with exactly similar ecological conditions. Futher, the variety *Partula suturalis vexillum* has recently spread from its earlier limited headquarters to the extremes of the main crescent of mountains, and it has changed from the direct to the reversed mode of coil in both directions. . . .

In brief, no discernible differences in external circumstances can be found to account for the occurrence of diverse combinations of species and varieties in the several habitable areas of Moorea, whether these are topographical sectors like the Rotui region, individual valleys, or subsidiary divisions of a single valley.

The further we carry the analysis of the individual colonies of the several species, the clearer it becomes that a factorial environment is excluded. Added to all of the foregoing citations we have at our disposal the abundant and universal facts of variation on the part of the characters of the snails in quantitative and qualitative respects, where the surroundings must be identical in any single association. The direction of the coil, size shape and coloration vary in ways that are completely explicable in terms of congenital causation; again we may cite the great value of the embryonic material in this connection. Other specific instances are noteworthy. The mutant dwarf of *Partula tohiveana* and the mutant giants of *Partula mooreana* in Oio and of *Partula sutur-*

alis in Urufara Valley can not be attributed to the incidence of peculiar external influences which have affected them alone and not other members of their communities. The excessively rare sinistral mutants of *Partula tæniata* were found in three separate localities which have no common peculiarity in ecological respects. Different color types are present in the brood-pouch of a single parent where all of the conditions other than those of innate nature must necessarily be the same. Finally, the instances cited where sinistral and dextral young appear in company apparently provide the most convincing proof that could be desired.

The evidences are cumulative, without any discrepancy, that so far as the present material is concerned the factors responsible for specific, varietal and lesser distinctions are congenital in nature and location, and that environmental circumstances produce no discernible effects upon the course of organic differentiation.

49

Australopithecus africanus: the man-ape of South Africa

RAYMOND A. DART

. . . The cercopithecid remains placed at our disposal certainly represent more than one species of catarrhine ape. The discovery of Cercopithecidæ in this area is not novel, for I have been informed that Mr. S. Haughton has in the press a paper discussing at least one species of baboon from this same spot (Royal Society of South Africa). It is of importance that, outside of the famous Fayüm area, primate deposits have been found on the African mainland at Oldaway, on the shores of Victoria Nyanza, and in Bechuanaland, for these discoveries lend promise to the expectation that a tolerably complete story of higher primate evolution in Africa will yet be wrested from our rocks.

In manipulating the pieces of rock brought back by Professor Young, I found that the larger natural endocranial cast articulated exactly by its fractured frontal extremity with another piece of rock in which the broken lower and posterior margin of the left side of a mandible was visible. After cleaning the rock mass, the outline of the hinder and lower part of the facial skeleton came into view. Careful development of the solid limestone in which it was embedded finally revealed the almost entire face. . . .

It was apparent when the larger endocranial cast was first observed that it was specially important, for its size and sulcal pattern revealed sufficient similarity with those of the chimpanzee and gorilla to demonstrate that one was handling in this instance an anthropoid and not a

Reprinted with the author's and publisher's permission from Nature, Vol. 115 (1925), pp. 195-199.

cercopithecid ape. Fossil anthropoids have not hitherto been recorded south of the Fayüm in Egypt, and living anthropoids have not been discovered in recent times south of Lake Kivu region in Belgian Congo, nearly 2000 miles to the north, as the crow flies.

All fossil anthropoids found hitherto have been known only from mandibular or maxillary fragments, so far as crania are concerned, and so the general appearance of the types they represented has been unknown; consequently, a condition of affairs where virtually the whole face and lower jaw, replete with teeth, together with the major portion of the brain pattern, have been preserved, constitutes a specimen of unusual value in fossil anthropoid discovery. Here, as in *Homo rhodesiensis,* Southern Africa has provided documents of higher primate evolution that are amongst the most complete extant.

Apart from this evidential completeness, the specimen is of importance because it exhibits an extinct race of apes *intermediate between living anthropoids and man.*

In the first place, the whole cranium displays *humanoid* rather than anthropoid lineaments. . . .

In the second place, the dentition is *humanoid* rather than anthropoid. . . .

In the third place, the mandible itself is *humanoid* rather than anthropoid. . . .

That hominid characters were not restricted to the face in this extinct primate group is borne out by the relatively forward situation of the foramen magnum. . . . It is significant that this index, which indicates in a measure the poise of the skull upon the vertebral column, points to the assumption by this fossil group of an attitude appreciably more erect than that of modern anthropoids. The improved poise of the head, and the better posture of the whole body framework which accompanied this alteration in the angle at which its dominant member was supported, is of great significance. It means that a greater reliance was being placed by this group upon the feet as organs of progression, and that the hands were being freed from their more primitive function of accessory organs of locomotion. . . .

Whether our present fossil is to be correlated with the discoveries made in India is not yet apparent; that question can only be solved by a careful comparison of the permanent molar teeth from both localities. It is obvious, meanwhile, that it represents a fossil group distinctly advanced beyond living anthropoids in those two dominantly human characters of facial and dental recession on one hand, and improved quality of the brain on the other. Unlike Pithecanthropus, it does not represent an ape-like man, a caricature of precocious hominid failure, but a creature well advanced beyond modern anthropoids in just those characters, facial and cerebral, which are to be anticipated in an extinct link between man and his simian ancestor. At the same time, it is equally evident that a creature with anthropoid brain capacity, and lacking the distinctive, localised temporal expansions which appear to be concomitant with and necessary to articulate man, is no true man. It is therefore logically regarded as a man-like ape. I propose tentatively, then, that a new family of *Homo-simiadæ* be created for the reception of the group of individuals which it represents, and that the first known species of the group be designated *Australopithecus africanus,* in commemoration, first, of the extreme southern and unexpected horizon of its discovery, and secondly, of the continent in which so many new and important discoveries connected with the early history of man have recently been made, thus vindicating the Darwinian claim that Africa would prove to be the cradle of mankind.

It will appear to many a remarkable fact that an ultrasimian and prehuman stock should be discovered, in the first place, at this extreme southern point in Africa, and, secondly, in Bechuanaland, for one does not associate with the present climatic conditions obtaining on the eastern fringe of the Kalahari desert an environment favourable to higher primate life. It is generally believed by geologists that the climate has fluctuated within exceedingly narrow limits in this country since Cretaceous times. We must therefore conclude that it was only the enhanced cerebral powers possessed by this group which made their existence possible in this untoward environment.

In anticipating the discovery of the true links between the apes and man in tropical countries, there has been a tendency to overlook the fact that, in the luxuriant forests of the tropical belts, nature was supplying with profligate and lavish hand an easy and sluggish solution, by adaptive specialisation, of the problem of existence in creatures so well equipped mentally as living anthropoids are. For the production of man a different apprenticeship was needed to sharpen the wits and quicken the higher manifestations of intellect — a more open veldt country where competition was keener between swiftness and stealth, and where adroitness of thinking and movement played a preponderating role in the preservation of the species. Darwin has said, "no country in the world abounds in a greater degree with dangerous beasts than Southern Africa," and, in my opinion, Southern Africa, by providing a vast open country with occasional wooded belts and a relative scarcity of water, together with a fierce and bitter mammalian competition, furnished a laboratory such as was essential to this penultimate phase of human evolution.

In Southern Africa, where climatic conditions appear to have fluctuated little since Cretaceous times, and where ample dolomitic formations have provided innumerable refuges during life and burial places after death for our troglodytic forefathers, we may confidently anticipate many complementary discoveries concerning this period in our evolution. . . .

50

adaptive changes induced by natural selection in wild populations of Drosophila

THEODOSIUS DOBZHANSKY

Recent observations have shown, however, that natural populations, even of higher organisms, sometimes undergo rapid adaptive changes. Some wild species react to seasonal alterations in their environment by cyclic modifications of their genetic structure. Knowing these facts, direct observation and experimentation on natural selection has become possible. Controlled experiments can now take the place of speculation as to what natural selection is or is not able to accomplish. . . .

In the corresponding Drosophila work, a character is used which is discernible only by microscopic examination of the larval salivary glands, namely the gene arrangement in the chromosomes. Variation of this character in species of Drosophila is due almost entirely to inversion of chromosome segments. Two or more such gene arrangements frequently occur in the same population. Since the carriers of different arrangements interbreed freely, some individuals have paired chromosomes with the same gene arrangements (inversion homozygotes) and others with unlike gene arrangements (inversion heterozygotes). . . .

Fifteen different gene arrangements are known in the third chromosome of *Drosophila pseudoobscura.* None of them occur in the entire distribution area of the species. Hence, there is no "normal" or "wild-type" gene arrangement. On the other hand, the populations of most localities contain more than one, and up to seven, gene arrangements. Because of the free interbreeding of the carriers of different arrange-

Reprinted with the author's and publisher's permission from Evolution, Vol. 1 (1947), pp. 1-16.

ments, many, frequently a majority, of wild individuals are inversion heterozygotes. The population of any locality can be described in terms of relative frequencies of different gene arrangements. The frequencies may differ in populations of different localities. . . .

About 50 per cent of third chromosomes in populations of south Coast Ranges of California have the so-called Standard gene arrangement. But the frequency of Standard falls to between 20 and 30 per cent in the Sierra Nevada and in the Death Valley regions which lie to the east of the Coast Ranges. Further east, in Arizona, the frequency falls to less than 5 per cent, and still further east Standard chromosomes occur but rarely. The Arrowhead gene arrangement is very common in Arizona and New Mexico, so much so that populations of some localities seem to be homozygous for it. But its frequency decreases eastward as well as westward from Arizona, reaching about 20 per cent in central Texas and in coastal California. The Pikes Peak gene arrangement is common in Texas, but rapidly decreases in frequency westward. . . .

Differences in the frequencies of gene arrangements may be observed however between populations which live in localities only a dozen or so miles apart. For example, three localities on Mount San Jacinto, California, were sampled repeatedly between 1939 and 1946. The approximate distances between these localities are 10 to 15 miles. One, Keen Camp, lies at an elevation of about 4500 feet in the ponderosa pine belt, the second, Piñon Flats, lies at 4000 feet in the much drier piñon forest, and the third, Andreas Canyon, lies at 800 feet on the desert's edge. . . .

. . . ST chromosomes are most frequent in the lowest locality, Andreas, and least frequent in the highest locality, Keen. CH chromosomes show the opposite relationship. No significant differences appear for AR chromosomes in the three localities. How common such altitudinal gradients are is an open question. Preliminary data suggest the existence of gradients among populations that occur at different elevations in the region of the Yosemite National Park, in the Sierra Nevada in California. . . .

The repeated samplings of the populations in the three localities on Mount San Jacinto (see above) have disclosed a very interesting fact, namely that the composition of a population may change quite significantly from month to month. Furthermore, these changes are regular and follow the annual cycle of seasons. In two of the three localities, namely at Piñon Flats and at Andreas Canyon, the changes are qualitatively similar. . . . the observations for all six years of collecting are grouped by months [and show] . . . that in spring (March) the population contains about 50 per cent of ST chromosomes and slightly more than 20 per cent CH chromosomes. From March to June the frequency of ST declines to less than 30 per cent and that of CH increases to just below 40 per cent. During the summer, from June to September, the reverse change takes place, namely ST increases in frequency, and CH decreases, to about the same values which these gene arrangements had during the spring. The changes of the frequencies of AR chromosomes are less regular than those of ST and CH, but on the whole AR seems to follow the same path as CH. No regular changes occur in the frequency of Tree Line chromosomes.

The changes at Andreas Canyon run parallel to those at Piñon Flats. . . .

Interestingly enough, a different kind of change has taken place in the Keen Camp population during the period of observation, from 1939 to 1946. Namely, there seems to exist a noncyclic, or at any rate nonseasonal, trend toward decreasing frequencies of AR and CH and increasing ones of ST chromosomes. In 1939, only 28 per cent of the third chromosomes found in the Keen locality had the ST gene arrangement; in 1942 the frequency rose to 36 per cent, and in 1946 to 50 per cent. The frequencies of AR and CH chromosomes in 1939 were 30 and 38 per cent respectively. In 1946 only 15 per cent of the chromosomes were AR and only about 28 per cent CH. No such directional trends of change have appeared at Piñon Flats or at Andreas Canyon, although statistically significant differences in the composition of the populations from year to year have been recorded also in these localities. . . .

The regular and cyclic nature of the changes observed in the populations of *D. pseudoobscura* on Mount San Jacinto can be most reasonably accounted for by natural selection as the prime causative factor. If during the spring the carriers of CH chromosomes leave more surviving progeny on the average than the carriers of ST chromosomes, then the frequency of CH will increase and that of ST will decrease. This is what happens from March to June. The reversal of the change during the summer months points toward the hypothesis that, in the summer environments, the carriers of ST chromosomes survive or reproduce on the average more often than do the carriers of CH chromosomes. The absence of changes during the autumn and winter at Andreas Canyon suggests that flies of different chromosomal types are equivalent in reaction to the environments prevailing during these seasons.

But the great rapidity of the observed changes constitutes an apparently serious argument against accounting for them on the ground of natural selection. Indeed, at Piñon Flats the frequency of ST chromosomes falls from about 50 per cent in March to 28 per cent in June, and increases again to about 48 per cent in September. Even though

Drosophila is a rapidly breeding insect, time intervals such as these can correspond to at most two to four generations. The selective forces that are necessary to bring about changes so swift as these must be very strong.

It should be remembered however that very little is known about the intensity of selective forces which operate in natural populations. The widespread opinion that these forces are generally weak, and their effects negligible except in terms of quasi-geological time is only an opinion and has no basis in factual data. To find in natural populations great selective pressures and the rapid changes produced by them may be unexpected but not inherently impossible. On the other hand, the occurrence of changes does not in itself prove that they are produced by natural selection. Such proof would be very difficult to adduce from observations of natural populations alone. The difficulty lies in the fact that, despite persistent effort, very little has been learned as yet about the food and shelter requirements of *D. pseudoobscura* in its natural habitats. . . .

Nevertheless, the postulated high selective advantages and disadvantages of the carriers of different gene arrangements in different environments has made practicable a still more ambitious project: to demonstrate the occurrence of natural selection by means of laboratory experiments. . . .

51

on the roles of directed and random changes in gene frequency in the genetics of populations

SEWALL WRIGHT

Science has largely advanced by the analytic procedure of isolating the effects of single factors in carefully controlled experiments. The task of science is not complete, however, without synthesis: the attempt to interpret natural phenomena in which numerous factors are varying simultaneously. Studies of the genetics of populations, including their evolution, present problems of this sort of the greatest complexity. Many writers on evolution have been inclined to ignore this and discuss the subject as if it were merely a matter of choosing between single factors. My own studies on population genetics have been guided primarily by the belief that a mathematical model must be sought which permits simultaneous consideration of all possible factors. Such a model must be sufficiently simple to permit a rough grasp of the system of interactions as a whole and sufficiently flexible to permit elaboration of aspects of which a more complete account is desired.

On attempting to make such a formulation it was at once apparent that any one of the factors might play the dominating role, at least for a time, under specifiable conditions, but it was concluded that in the long run "evolution as a process of cumulative change depends on a proper balance of the conditions which at each level of organization – gene, chromosome, cell, individual, local race – make for genetic homogeneity or genetic heterogeneity of the species."

Reprinted with the author's and publisher's permission from Evolution, Vol. 2 (1948), pp. 279-294.

The purpose of the present paper is to reiterate this point of view in connection with certain misapprehensions which have arisen. . . .

In spite of his repeated emphasis on dynamic equilibrium among all factors as the most favorable condition for evolution, the author has often been credited with advocating the all importance of a single factor, viz. sampling effects in very small populations. Thus in Goldschmidt's stimulating book "The Material Basis of Evolution" he states: "The adherents of such a view" (NeoDarwinism) "derive much comfort from the results of population mathematics, especially Wright's calculation (1931) showing that small isolated groups have the greatest chance of accumulating mutants even without favorable selection. . . . It is the contention that small isolated populations have the greatest chances from the standpoint of population mathematics." What I actually stated on this matter in the summary of the paper referred to was as follows: "In too small a population there is nearly complete fixation, little variation, little effect of selection and thus a static condition, modified occasionally by chance fixation of rare mutations, leading inevitably to degeneration and extinction." The same conclusion has been reiterated in all more recent general discussions.

This misapprehension may have arisen from the emphasis put on population structure later in the same summary: "Finally in a large population, divided and subdivided into partially isolated local races of small size, there is a continually shifting differentiation among the latter, intensified by local differences in selection, but occurring under uniform and static conditions, which inevitably brings about an indefinitely continuing, irreversible, adaptive, and much more rapid evolution of the species" (than in a comparably large, random-breeding population). It should be noted that a favorable population structure, under this view, may be prevented by excessive density of population, as well as by too small a total number. The implied relation of size of population to rate of evolution is not a simple one. I suspect that "inevitably" is too strong a word as used above, but otherwise this quotation still represents my position on the importance of population structure in evolution. The ways in which it is important were, of course, brought out more completely elsewhere in this paper and have been developed further in later papers.

This leads to consideration of a recent inaccurate statement of my views by R. A. Fisher and E. B. Ford. Their first reference is in the main an acceptable statement of the role which I have attributed to random shifts in gene frequencies, provided that the word "partially" is inserted before "isolated" and it is clearly understood that the primary significance of the process is as one of a number of adjuncts to intergroup selection. "Great evolutionary importance has been attached by Sewall Wright to the fact that small shifts in the gene ratios of all segregating factors will occur from generation to generation owing to the errors of random sampling in the process by which the gametes available in any one generation are chosen to constitute the next. Such chance deviations will, of course, be greater the smaller the isolated population concerned. Wright believes that such nonadaptive changes in gene ratio may serve an evolutionary purpose by permitting the occurrence of genotypes harmoniously adapted to their environment in ways not yet explored and so of opening up new evolutionary possibilities."

The next sentence indicates, however, that the authors have wholly missed the major point stressed in all of the cited papers. "Consequently he claims that subdivision into isolated groups of small size is favorable to evolutionary progress not as others have held through the variety of environmental conditions to which such colonies are exposed but even if the environment were the same for all, through nonadaptive and casual changes favored by small population size." Actually the point stressed most in these papers was the simultaneous treatment of all factors by the inclusion of coefficients measuring the effects of all of them on gene frequency in a single formula. Thus in the 1931 paper the formula for distribution of gene frequencies in a partially isolated local population included the coefficient N_1 for effective size of the local population, s_1 for selection due to local conditions, m_1 for rate of immigration and q_m for gene frequency among the immigrants (mutation pressure was here assumed to be the same throughout the species). This simultaneous treatment made it possible to specify the conditions under which one or another process would dominate with respect to a particular gene. Sampling fluctuations were treated as only one of a number of processes which lead to trial and error among local populations. This has been reiterated in all later discussions. . . .

Fisher and Ford continue with an analysis of annual fluctuations of the frequency of a certain gene in an isolated population of the moth *Panaxia dominula*. They decide that the fluctuations are too great to have been due to accidents of sampling and hence conclude that they must have been due to fluctuations in the action of selection. They arrive at the following generalization.

"The conclusion that natural populations in general, like that to which this study is devoted, are affected by selective action, varying from time to time in direction and intensity and of sufficient magnitude to cause fluctuating variations in all gene frequencies is in good accordance with other studies of observable frequencies in wild populations. We do not think, however, that it has been sufficiently emphasized that this fact is fatal to the theory which ascribes particular evolutionary importance to such fluctuations in gene ratios as may occur by chance in very small isolated populations. . . . Thus our analysis, the first in which the relative parts played by random survival and selection in a wild population can be tested, does not support the view that chance fluctuations can be of any significance in evolution."

Thus Fisher and Ford insist on an either-or antithesis according to which one must either hold that the fluctuations of *all* gene frequencies that are of any evolutionary significance are due to accidents of sampling (attributed to me) or that they are *all* due to differences in selection, which they adopt. As already noted, I have consistently rejected this antithesis and have consistently accepted both sorts as playing important, complementary, and interacting roles. According to the criteria developed in the 1931 paper and later, the genes in a population may be put into 3 classes with respect to the roles of selection and random sampling. One class of segregating genes in any population may be expected to be almost wholly dominated by selection in one way or another, another class almost wholly by accidents of sampling, while an intermediate class, to which special importance was attributed, will show important joint effects. . . .

52

industrial melanism in the Lepidoptera and its contribution to our knowledge of evolution

H. B. D. KETTLEWELL

Industrial melanism refers to the phenomenon, at present taking place in the Lepidoptera of many countries, in which whole populations are changing from light to dark coloration. It is in fact the most striking evolutionary change ever witnessed in our lifetime. It has been referred to as a transient polymorphism: but polymorphism, wherever found, must be accepted as offering an opportunity for research. The fact that two or more forms of a species exist within a population must surely suggest alternative advantages, or disadvantages, for each, and these are, quite definitely, not limited to colour differences alone, but to the whole behaviour and physiological pattern of the individuals concerned. In transient polymorphism, we are witnessing a situation in its acute phase. Much more frequently we meet it in a balanced state in which the environment, with comparatively little change, governs the proportions of the two or more forms in a population. Industrial melanism may, therefore, be regarded as an expression of the degree of change which has taken place due to the impact of civilization. It also reflects the speed at which living organisms can adapt themselves to a changed situation.

In England, since the middle of the last century, black forms of many species have been becoming increasingly common, and at the present moment more than seventy species in the British Isles are in the process of changing. One of the earliest to do this was *Biston betularia* L.,

Reprinted with the author's and publisher's permission from the Proceedings of the 10th International Congress of Entomology (Montreal), Vol. 2 (1958), pp. 831-841.

the Peppered Moth. Its all black form, *carbonaria* Jordan, was first recorded about 1845 from Manchester, when at its highest frequency it could not have been more than one per cent of the population. By 1895, however, it formed about 99 per cent. J. B. S. Haldane has shown that this represents an approximate 30 per cent advantage of the black form over the light for this period, a figure hitherto unknown in selective advantages. Since then, the same has taken place in scores of other species, but it must be noted that these are limited to those which depend for survival on their cryptic coloration, species which rely on their colour protection and pass the day concealed sitting motionless on lichened tree trunks, boughs or rocks. Industrial melanism does not normally occur among species which depend on other types of defence, such as warning or flash coloration, nor amongst those which simulate dead leaves or green foliage.

In nearly every case it has been shown that the new black mutant is inherited as a simple Mendelian dominant, and in no case so far investigated has a recessive melanic spread through the population. Recessive melanics do, however, occur, but these are for the most part confined to non-cryptic species. They are rare, semilethal and are maintained by recurrent mutation. . . .

Using *Biston betularia,* we have recently been able to show the important part played by natural selection. By releasing known numbers of marked individuals into first of all an industrial area, where the local population consisted of nearly 90 per cent melanics, and secondly into unpolluted countryside, where there were no melanics, the selective advantages of the two forms in each case have been ascertained. Of 584 individuals (447 *carbonaria* and 137 *typical*) freed into the Birmingham area, we got back three time more *carbonaria* than *typical.* However, in the release of 969 *betularia* into an unpolluted wood in Dorset, we found exactly the reverse and recovered three times more of the *typical* light form than *carbonaria.* Furthermore, Dr. Niko Tinbergen was able to film six species of birds in the act of taking the moths at rest and *they did this selectively.* By eliminating other considerations, it was possible to show that selective predation was responsible for the deficiency in each case. In my opinion, there can be no longer any doubt of the part played by birds in the selective elimination of those individuals which do not conform to their backgrounds.

But this need not necessarily be the only difference between the black and the light forms. The gene responsible for the changed line of chemistry of the pigment is also responsible for other, maybe equally important, physiological and behaviour differences. We have attempted to analyse some of these. E. B. Ford has previously shown that when subjected to a degree of starvation, the melanic form of *Alcis repandata f. nigra* is more hardy than its *typical* form. . . .

In this light, industrial melanism may confer on a species a capacity for extending its larval life later in the season than would otherwise be the case.

There is some evidence that in certain backcross broods originating from industrial areas those larvæ which fed up rapidly and pupated first produced a high proportion of *typical betularia,* whilst those that fed slowly and pupated late in the summer were mostly of the *carbonaria* form. . . .

Lastly, there may be a difference between the two forms in regard to their choice of resting site by day. Into a large barrel which presented alternate surface areas of black and white, equal numbers of each form of *B. betularia* were introduced at night; and at daybreak they were scored for correct or incorrect positions. Those individuals which were on the edges or the top or bottom of the container were eliminated. Of 118 releases which qualified, 77 chose correct positions, and 41 incorrect. It is likely, therefore, that the two forms are sensitive to the background they choose, having regard to their own colour. The same mechanism could account for their behaviour in each case. It is possible that contrast differences between the colour of the scales surrounding the eyes and the light reflected from the background on which they sit are appreciated and gauged by the different segments of the eye. In over 2,000 releases of *B. betularia* in the field, I have frequently noted that the insects take up the best possible position presented locally, and before settling down finally, they revolve on their own axis at the same time as they flatten their wings against the trunks. It is possible that during this procedure they are testing contrast differences.

These then, apart from changed pigmentation, are indications of the existence of behaviour differences between the dark and light forms. It must be emphasized, however, that in none of these have investigations been carried out, so far, on a scale large enough to admit conclusive results. If these differences really exist, some conferring benefits, others disadvantages, a state of balanced polymorphism may be expected to be attained in many species, and this is the more likely if the heterozygous melanic is at an advantage to both the homozygous forms.

Lastly, we have attempted to formulate a theory for the origin of the industrial melanics and the reason for their being Mendelian dominants in nearly every case. Dominance suggests that the gene-complex must have, at some time in the past, had previous experience of the particular mutation, that it was successful, and that during this period the state of dominance was achieved. It in no way assumes, however, that the conditions under which these melanics flourished bear any relationship to those found today as the result of industrialization. Conversely, it could be argued that a recessive melanic has previously on no occasion conferred benefits on the species and hence, in a gene-complex not fitted to receive it, it is driven into the recessive state. . . .

ECOSYSTEM LEVEL OF ORGANIZATION

Natural History and Modern Ecology

At the ecosystem level of organization, a more comprehensive view of the organism is in order. The myriad relationships obtaining within an organism and within or between populations are made more complex when interactions with the environment are superimposed. At this level the totality of relationships must be synthesized. It is paradoxical that this is the one aspect of biology which extends to antiquity in the form of natural history and is, as yet, the least developed comprehensively and conceptually of all aspects of biology.

The spirit of geographic and intellectual adventure is found in the following selections on natural history and biogeography. In only small measure is geographic exploration any longer a vigorous component of modern biology, not that this may not be regretted. The boldness and daring of some intrepid explorers was matched sometimes more by their imagination than by accuracy of observation. Setting aside these weaknesses, it was through the efforts of such chroniclers and early second-hand observers as Aristotle (p. 196) and Theophrastus (p. 199) that early biology was preserved for later refinement. In Alexander von Humboldt, however, we find exemplified the keen, almost poetic, astute explorer and investigator – the kind who opened new horizons and posed new questions. The travels of von Humboldt in the early 1800s (p. 202), like those of Darwin, Hooker and others, not only opened the New World in the geographic sense but in the intellectual sense as well.

No less exacting in a day when it is the boundaries of outer space that are being explored was the time a century ago when it was the unknown depths of the sea which challenged (as they continue to do) man's scientific best. The pioneer of the sea, particularly in the famous expeditions of the Challenger, was C. Wyville Thomson. His early studies on the sea are remarkable (p. 206).

Accumulating observations led inevitably to recognition of distributional patterns of plants and animals. There logically followed a seeking of causes of these peculiar distributional patterns. One of the major foci of late nineteenth and early twentieth century biology was concern with biogeography and is evidenced here in the writing of Schimper on plants (p. 216) and of Merriam on animals (p. 212).

Modern ecology is decidedly rooted in the great tradition of natural history and biogeography; there is still in many an ecologist a touch of the naturalist. Yet, the term naturalist in current connotation suggests a less systematic and more anecdotal kind of biology, one that does not provide the solid framework required for testable hypothesis and theory construction.

The essence of what is now considered to be modern ecology was perhaps best stated in a late nineteenth century paper by Stephen Forbes (p. 209). Forbes comprehensive view of the microcosm, which he saw and described in an Illinois farm pond, is what today is referred to as an ecosystem, an interacting unit of nature in which there is energy and matter dependence. A modern statement on the ecosystem is best expressed by its foremost proponent, Eugene Odum (p. 238).

The study of ecology is, however, most varied. The selection from Shelford (p. 222) shows one aspect – a concern with the nature of the impinging environment and the response of organisms to it. Hutchinson's paper (p. 234) takes a different tack in demonstrating the mutual interacting regulation of environment and organism. The binding element of the ecosystem, energy, found its first articulate expression in 1927 in Charles Elton's concept of the food chain (p. 226). In 1942 a more sophisticated treatment was developed by Raymond Lindeman who specified the energetic-dynamics of the ecosystem, especially as it undergoes succession (p. 230). Yet another facet of ecology is reflected in the paper by Eugene Warming in 1909 (p. 219). Warming gave direction to the field of plant ecology for many years by considering the association of plants in particular areas largely apart from the dynamic interplay of other components of the community.

53

the history of animals

ARISTOTLE

1. Animals are divided according to the localities which they inhabit; for some animals are terrestrial, others are aquatic. They also admit of a ternary division, those that breathe air and those that breathe water, one of these classes is terrestrial, the other is aquatic; the third class does not breathe either air or water, but they are adapted by nature to receive refreshment from each of these elements; and some of these are called terrestrial, others are aquatic, though they breathe neither air nor water; and there are other animals which procure their food and make their abode in either of these elements. For many that breathe air, and produce their young upon the land, procure their food from the water, where they generally make their abode; and these are the only animals which appear to be doubtful, for they may be arranged either as terrestrial or aquatic animals.

2. Of those that breathe water, none have feet or wings, nor seek their food on land; but many of those that are terrestrial, and breathe air, do so; some of them so much so that they cannot live when separated from the water, as those which are called marine turtles, and crocodiles, and hippopotami, and seals, and some of the smaller creatures, as the water tortoise and the frog tribe; for all these are suffocated if their respiration is suspended for any length of time. They produce their young and rear them on dry land; others do so near the dry land, while they reside in the water.

Excerpts from Chapter VIII of Historia Animalia (c. 350 B.C.) as translated by Richard Cresswell. Henry G. Bohn, London (1862).

3. Of all animals the most remarkable in this particular is the dolphin, and some other aquatic animals and cetacea which are of this habit, as the whale and others which have a blowhole; for it is not easy to arrange them either with aquatic or terrestrial animals, if we consider animals that breathe air as terrestrial, and those that breathe water as aquatics, for they partake of the characters of both classes; for they receive the sea and eject it through their blowhole, and air through their lungs, for they have this part, and breathe through it. And the dolphin, when captured in nets, is often suffocated from the impossibility of breathing. It will live for a long while out of water, snoring and groaning like other breathing animals. It sleeps with its snout above the water, in order that it may breathe through it.

4. It is thus impossible to arrange it under both of these contrary divisions, but it would appear that the aquatic animals must be further subdivided; for they breathe and eject water for the same reason as others breathe air, for the sake of coolness. Other animals do this for the sake of food; for those animals which obtain their food in the water must also, at the same time, swallow some of the fluid and have an organ by which they can eject it. Those creatures which use water instead of air for breathing have gills; those that use it for food have a blowhole. These creatures are sanguineous. The nature of the malacia and malacostraca is the same; for these swallow water for food.

5. Those animals which breathe air, but live in the water, and those which breathe water, and have gills, but go out upon dry land and take their food there, belong to two divisions of aquatic animals. This last division is represented by a single animal called the cordylus (water newt); for this animal has no lungs, but gills; and it goes on dry land to procure its food. It has four feet, so that it appears natural that it should walk. In all these animals nature appears to be, as it were, turned aside, and some of the males appear to be females, and the females have a male appearance; for animals which have but small diversity in particular parts exhibit great variations in the whole body. . . .

1. All birds with crooked claws are carnivorous, nor are they able to eat corn even when put in their mouths. All the eagles belong to this class and the kites, and both the hawks, the pigeon hawk namely, and the sparrow hawk. These differ in size from each other, and so does the triorches. This bird is as large as the kite, and is visible at all seasons of the year; the osprey and vulture also belong to this class. The osprey is as large as the eagle, and ash-coloured. There are two kinds of vultures, one small and whitish, the other large and cinereous. . . .

1. Animals covered with scaly plates, as the lizard and other quadrupeds and serpents, are omnivorous, for they eat both flesh and grass,

and serpents lick their prey more than any other animal; all these creatures, and indeed all with spongy lungs, drink very little, and all that are oviparous are of this kind and have but little blood. Serpents are all very fond of wine, so that they hunt the viper by placing vessels of wine in the hedgerows, and they are captured when intoxicated. Serpents devour any animal that they may have captured, and when they have sucked out the juice, they reject all the remainder; nearly all such animals do this, as also the spiders. But the spiders suck the juice without swallowing the animal. Serpants suck the juice internally.

2. The serpent swallows any food which may be presented to it, for it will devour both birds and beasts, and suck eggs. When it has taken its food it draws itself up, till it stands erect upon its extremity, it then gathers itself up and contracts itself a little, so that when stretched out the animal it has swallowed may descend in its stomach; it does this because its œsophagus is long and thin. Phalangia and serpents can live a long while without food, this may be seen in those that are kept by dealers in medicine. . . .

1. All the actions of animals are employed either in sexual intercourse, or in rearing their young, or in procuring food for themselves, or in providing against excessive heat and cold, and the changes of the seasons. For they all have naturally a sensitiveness respecting heat and cold, and, like mankind, who either change their abodes in cold weather, or those who have large estates, pass their summer in cold countries and their winter in warm ones; so animals, also, if they can, migrate from place to place. Some of them find protection in their accustomed localities, others are migratory; and at the autumnal equinox, escape at the approach of winter, from the Pontus and other cold places; and in spring retreat again before the approach of summer from hot to cold countries, for they are afraid of excessive heat. Some migrate from places close at hand, and others from the very ends of the earth. . . .

1. It has already been observed that fish migrate from the deep water to the coast, and from the coast to the deep water, in order to avoid the excesses of cold and heat. Those that frequent the neighbourhood of the coast are better than those from deep water, for the feeding grounds are better and more abundant. For wherever the sun strikes the plants are more frequent, and superior, and more delicate, as in gardens, and the black shore-weed grows near the land, and the other kinds rather resemble uncultivated plants. The neighbourhood of the coast is also more temperate, both in heat and cold, than the rest of the sea; for which reason the flesh of fish which live near the shore is more compact, while that of fish from deep sea is watery and soft. . . .

54

of the trees and plants special to particular districts and positions

THEOPHRASTUS

I. The differences between trees of the same kind have already been considered. Now all grow fairer and are more vigorous in their proper positions; for wild, no less than cultivated trees, have each their own positions: some love wet and marshy ground, as black poplar, abele, willow, and in general those that grow by rivers; some love exposed and sunny positions; some prefer a shady place. The fir is fairest and tallest in a sunny position, and does not grow at all in a shady one; the silver fir on the contrary is fairest in a shady place, and not so vigorous in a sunny one.

Thus there is in Arcadia near the place called Krane a low-lying district sheltered from wind, into which they say that the sun never strikes; and in this district the silver firs excel greatly in height and stoutness, though they have not such close grain nor such comely wood, but quite the reverse – like the fir when it grows in a shady place. Wherefore men do not use these for expensive work, such as doors or other choice articles, but rather for shipbuilding and house building. For excellent rafters, beams and yardarms are made from these, and also masts of great length which are not however equally strong; while masts made of trees grown in a sunny place are necessarily short but of closer grain and stronger than the others.

Yew *pados* and joint-fir rejoice exceedingly in shade. On mountain tops and in cold positions odorous cedar grows even to a height, while

Reprinted by permission of the publishers from Loeb Classical Library, Theophrastus, Enquiry into plants (c. 300 B.C.), translated by Sir Arthur Hort. G. P. Putnam's Sons, New York (1916).

silver fir and Phoenician cedar grow, but not to a height – for instance on the top of Mount Cyllene; and holly also grows in high and very wintry positions. These trees then we may reckon as cold-loving; all others, one may say in general, prefer a sunny position. However this too depends partly on the soil appropriate to each tree; thus they say that in Crete on the mountains of Ida and on those called the White Mountains the cypress is found on the peaks whence the snow never disappears; for this is the principal tree both in the island generally and in the mountains.

Again, as has been said already, both of wild and of cultivated trees some belong more to the mountains, some to the plains. And on the mountains themselves in proportion to the height some grow fairer and more vigorous in the lower regions, some about the peaks. However it is true of all trees anywhere that with a north aspect the wood is closer and more compact and better generally; and, generally speaking, more trees grow in positions facing the north. Again trees which are close together grow and increase more in height, and so become unbranched straight and erect, and the best oar-spars are made from these, while those that grow far apart are of greater bulk and denser habit; wherefore they grow less straight and with more branches, and in general have harder wood and a closer grain.

Such trees exhibit nearly the same differences, whether the position be shady or sunny, windless or windy; for trees growing in a sunny or windy position are more branched, shorter and less straight. Further that each tree seeks an appropriate position and climate is plain from the fact that some districts bear some trees but not others; (the latter do not grow there of their own accord, nor can they easily be made to grow), and that, even if they obtain a hold, they do not bear fruit – as was said of the date palm, the sycamore and others; for there are many trees which in many places either do not grow at all, or, if they do, do not thrive nor bear fruit, but are in general of inferior quality. And perhaps we should discuss this matter, so far as our enquiries go. . . .

VI. However the greatest difference in the natural character itself of trees and of tree-like plants generally we must take to be that mentioned already, namely, that of plants, as of animals, some belong to the earth, some to water. Not only in swamps, lakes and rivers, but even in the sea there are some tree-like growths, and in the ocean there are even trees. In our own sea all the things that grow are small, and hardly any of them rise above the surface; but in the ocean we find the same kinds rising above the surface, and also other larger trees.

Those found in our own waters are as follows: most conspicuous of those which are of general occurrence are seaweed, oyster-green and the like; most obvious of those peculiar to certain parts are the sea plants called "fir," "fig," "oak," "vine," "palm." Of these some are found close to land, others in the deep sea, others equally in both positions. And some have many forms, as seaweed, some but one. Thus of seaweed there is the broad-leaved kind, riband-like and green in colour, which some call "green-weed" and others "girdle-weed." This has a root which on the outside is shaggy, but the inner part is made of several coats, and it is fairly long and stout, like *kromyogeteion* (a kind of onion).

Another kind has hair-like leaves like fennel, and is not green but pale yellow; nor has it a stalk, but it is, as it were, erect in itself; this grows on oyster shells and stones, not, like the other, attached to the bottom; but both are plants of the shore, and the hair-leaved kind grows close to land, and sometimes is merely washed over by the sea; while the other is found further out.

Again in the ocean about the pillars of Heracles there is a kind of marvellous size, they say, which is larger, about a palmsbreadth. This is carried into the inner sea along with the current from the outer sea, and they call it "sea-leek" (riband-weed); and in this sea in some parts it grows higher than a man's waist. It is said to be annual and to come up at the end of spring, and to be at its best in summer, and to wither in autumn, while in winter it perishes and is thrown up on shore. Also, they say, all the other plants of the sea become weaker and feebler in winter. These then are, one may say, the sea plants which are found near the shore. But the "seaweed of ocean," which is dived for by the sponge fishers, belongs to the open sea. . . .

55

the island of Teneriffe

ALEXANDER von HUMBOLDT

The valley of Tacoronte is the entrance into that charming country, of which travellers of every nation have spoken with rapturous enthusiasm. Under the torrid zone I found sites where nature is more majestic and richer in the display of organic forms; but after having traversed the banks of the Orinoco, the Cordilleras of Peru, and the most beautiful valleys of Mexico, I own that I have never beheld a prospect more varied, more attractive, more harmonious in the distribution of the masses of verdure and of rocks than the western coast of Teneriffe.

The seacoast is lined with date and cocoa trees. Groups of the musa, as the country rises, form a pleasing contrast with the dragon tree, the trunks of which have been justly compared to the tortuous form of the serpent. The declivities are covered with vines, which throw their branches over towering poles. Orange trees loaded with flowers, myrtles, and cypress trees encircle the chapels reared to devotion on the isolated hills. The divisions of landed property are marked by hedges formed of the agave and the cactus. An innummerable quantity of cryptogamous plants, among which ferns are the most predominant, cover the walls, and are moistened by small springs of limpid water. In winter, when the volcano is buried under ice and snow, this district enjoys perpetual spring. In summer, as the day declines, the breezes from the sea diffuse a delicious freshness. The population of this coast is very con-

Reprinted from the Personal narrative of travels to the equinoctial regions of America during the years 1799-1804, translated by Thomasina Ross. G. Bell and Sons, London (1851).

siderable; and it appears to be still greater than it is, because the houses and gardens are distant from each other, which adds to the picturesque beauty of the scene. Unhappily the real welfare of the inhabitants does not correspond with the exertions of their industry, or with the advantages which nature has lavished on this spot. The farmers are not landowners; the fruits of their labour belong to the nobles; and those feudal institutions, which, for so long a time, spread misery throughout Europe, still press heavily on the people of the Canary Islands.

From Tegueste and Tacoronte to the village of St. Juan de la Rambla (which is celebrated for its excellent malmsey wine), the rising hills are cultivated like a garden. I might compare them to the environs of Capua and Valentia, if the western part of Teneriffe was not infinitely more beautiful on account of the proximity of the peak, which presents on every side a new point of view. The aspect of this mountain is interesting not merely from its gigantic mass; it excites the mind, by carrying it back to the mysterious source of its volcanic agency. For thousands of years, no flames or light have been perceived on the summit of the Piton, nevertheless enormous lateral eruptions, the last of which took place in 1798, are proofs of the activity of a fire still far from being extinguished. There is also something that leaves a melancholy impression on beholding a crater in the centre of a fertile and well-cultivated country. The history of the globe informs us that volcanoes destroy what they have been a long series of ages in creating. Islands, which the action of submarine fires has raised above the waters, are by degrees clothed in rich and smiling verdure; but these new lands are often laid waste by the renewed action of the same power which caused them to emerge from the bottom of the ocean. Islets, which are now but heaps of scoriæ and volcanic ashes, were once perhaps as fertile as the hills of Tacoronte and Sauzal. Happy the country where man has no distrust of the soil on which he lives! . . .

The establishment of a botanical garden at Teneriffe is a very happy idea on account of the influence it is likely to have on the progress of botany, and on the introduction of useful plants into Europe. For the first conception of it we are indebted to the Marquis de Nava. He undertook, at an enormous expense, to level the hill of Durasno, which rises as an amphitheatre, and which was begun to be planted in 1795. The marquis thought that the Canary Islands, from the mildness of their climate and geographical position, were the most suitable place for naturalising the productions of the East and West Indies, and for inuring the plants gradually to the colder temperature of the south of Europe. The plants of Asia, Africa, and South America may easily be brought to Orotava; and in order to introduce the bark-tree into Sicily, Portugal, or Grenada, it should be first planted at Durasno, or at Laguna, and the shoots of this tree may afterwards be transported into Europe from the Canaries. In happier times, when maritime wars shall no longer interrupt communication, the garden of Teneriffe may become extremely useful with respect to the great number of plants which are sent from the Indies to Europe; for ere they reach our coasts, they often perish, owing to the length of the passage, during which they inhale an air impregnated with salt water. These plants would meet at Orotava with the care and climate necessary for their preservation. . . .

About three in the morning, by the sombrous light of a few fir torches, we started on our journey to the summit of the Piton. We scaled the volcano on the northeast side, where the declivities are extremely steep; and after two hours' toil, we reached a small plain, which, on account of its elevated position, bears the name of Alta Vista. This is the station of the *neveros,* those natives whose occupation it is to collect ice and snow, which they sell in the neighbouring towns. Their mules, better practised in climbing mountains than those hired by travellers, reach Alta Vista, and the *neveros* are obliged to transport the snow to that place on their backs. Above this point commences the Malpays, a term by which is designated here, as well as in Mexico, Peru, and every other country subject to volcanoes, a ground destitute of vegetable mould, and covered with fragments of lava. . . .

When we gained the summit of the Piton, we were surprised to find scarcely room enough to seat ourselves conveniently. We were stopped by a small circular wall of porphyritic lava, with a base of pitchstone, which concealed from us the view of the crater. The west wind blew with such violence that we could scarcely stand. It was eight in the morning, and we suffered severely from the cold, though the thermometer kept a little above freezing point. For a long time we had been accustomed to a very high temperature, and the dry wind increased the feeling of cold, because it carried off every moment the small atmosphere of warm and humid air which was formed around us from the effect of cutaneous perspiration.

The brink of the crater of the peak bears no resemblance to those of most of the other volcanoes which I have visited: for instance, the craters of Vesuvius, Jorullo, and Pichincha. In these the Piton preserves its conic figure to the very summit: the whole of their declivity is inclined the same number of degrees, and uniformly covered with a layer of pumice stone very minutely divided; when we reach the top of these volcanoes, nothing obstructs the view of the bottom of the crater. The peaks of Teneriffe and Cotopaxi, on the contrary, are of very different construction. At their summit a circular wall surrounds the crater; which wall, at a distance, has the appearance of a small cylinder placed on a truncated cone. On Cotopaxi this peculiar construction is visible to the naked eye at more than 2,000 toises distance; and no person has ever reached the crater of that volcano. On the peak of Teneriffe, the wall, which surrounds the crater like a parapet, is so high that it would be impossible to reach the Caldera, if, on the eastern side, there was not a breach, which seems to have been the effect of a flowing of very old lava. We descended through this breach toward the bottom of the funnel, the figure of which is elliptic. . . .

56

the depths of the sea

C. WYVILLE THOMSON

During the several cruises of H.M. ships "Lightning" and "Porcupine" in the years 1868, 1869, and 1870, fifty-seven hauls of the dredge were taken in the Atlantic at depths beyond 500 fathoms, and sixteen at depths beyond 1,000 fathoms, and in cases life was abundant. In 1869 we took two casts in depths greater than 2,000 fathoms. In both of these life was abundant; and with the deepest cast, 2,435 fathoms, off the mouth of the Bay of Biscay, we took living, well-marked and characteristic examples of all of the five invertebrate sub-kingdoms. And thus the question of the existence of abundant animal life at the bottom of the sea has been finally settled and for all depths, for there is no reason to suppose that the depth anywhere exceeds between three and four thousand fathoms; and if there be nothing in the conditions of a depth of 2,500 fathoms to prevent the full development of a varied fauna, it is impossible to suppose that even an additional thousand fathoms would make any great difference.

The conditions which might be expected principally to affect animal life at great depths of the sea are pressure, temperature, and the absence of light which apparently involves the absence of vegetable food.

After passing a zone surrounding the land, which is everywhere narrow compared with the extent of the ocean, through which the bottom more or less abruptly shelves downwards and the water deepens;

Reprinted from the introduction. Published by The Macmillan Co., London (1873) speaking very generally, the average depth of the sea is 2,000 fathoms, or about two miles; as far below the surface as the average height of the Swiss Alps. In some places the depth seems to be considerably greater, possibly here and there nearly double that amount; but these abysses are certainly very local, and their existence is even uncertain, and a vast portion of the area does not reach a depth of 1,500 fathoms.

The enormous pressure at these great depths seemed at first sight alone sufficient to put any idea of life out of the question. There was a curious popular notion, in which I well remember sharing when a boy, that, in going down, the seawater became gradually under the pressure heavier and heavier, and that all the loose things in the sea floated at different levels, according to their specific weight: skeletons of men, anchors and shot and cannon, and last of all the broad gold pieces wrecked in the loss of many a galleon on the Spanish Main; the whole forming a kind of "false bottom" to the ocean, beneath which there lay all the depth of clear still water, which was heavier than molten gold.

The conditions of pressure are certainly very extraordinary. At 2,000 fathoms a man would bear upon his body a weight equal to twenty locomotive engines, each with a long goods train loaded with pig iron. We are apt to forget, however, that water is almost incompressible, and that therefore the density of sea water at a depth of 2,000 fathoms is scarcely appreciably increased. At the depth of a mile, under a pressure of about 159 atmospheres, sea water, according to the formula given by Jamin, is compressed by the $\frac{1}{144}$ of its volume; and at twenty miles, supposing the law of the compressibility to continue the same, by only $\frac{1}{7}$ of its volume — that is to say, the volume at that depth would be $\frac{6}{7}$ of the volume of the same weight of water at the surface. . . .

The question of the distribution of heat in the sea, which is one of the greatest interests in connection with the distribution of marine animals, will be fully discussed in a future chapter. The broad conclusions to which we have been led by late investigations are that instead of there being a permanent deep layer of water at 4° C., the average temperature of the bottom of the deep sea in temperate and tropical regions is about 0° C., the freezing point of fresh water; and that there is a general surface movement of warm water, produced probably by a combination of various causes, from the equatorial regions towards the poles, and a slow undercurrent, or rather indraught, of cold water from the poles towards the equator. . . . That a cold flow from the polar seas passes over the bottom seems to be proved by the fact that in all parts of the world wherever deep temperature soundings have been taken, from the arctic circle to the equator, the temperature sinks with increasing depth, and is lower at the bottom than the normal temperature of the crust of the earth; an evidence that a constantly renewed supply of cold water is cooling down the surface of the crust, which, being a bad conductor, does not transmit heat with sufficient rapidity to affect perceptibly the temperature of the cold indraught. . . .

The temperature of the sea apparently never sinks at any depth below – 3.5°C., a degree of cold which, singularly enough, is not inconsistent with abundant and vigorous animal life, so that in the ocean, except perhaps within the eternal ice barrier of the antarctic pole, life seems nowhere to be limited by cold. But although certain sea animals – many of them, such as the siphonophora, the salpæ, and the ctenophorous medusæ, of the most delicate and complicated organization – are tolerant of such severe cold, it would appear to be temperature almost entirely which regulates the distribution of species. . . .

We have as yet very little exact knowledge as to the distance to which the sun's light penetrates into the water of the sea. According to some recent experiments which will be referred to in a future chapter, it would appear that the rays capable of affecting a delicate photographic film are very rapidly cut off, their effect being imperceptible at the depth of only a few fathoms. It is probable that some portions of the sun's light possessing certain properties may penetrate to a much greater distance, but it must be remembered that even the clearest sea water is more or less tinted by suspended opaque particles and floating organisms, so that the light has more than a pure saline solution to contend with. At all events it is certain that beyond the first 50 fathoms plants are barely represented, and after 200 fathoms they are entirely absent. The question of the mode of nutrition of animals at great depths becomes, therefore, a very singular one. . . .

57

the lake as a microcosm

STEPHEN A. FORBES

A lake . . . forms a little world within itself – a microcosm within which all the elemental forces are at work and the play of life goes on in full, but on so small a scale as to bring it easily within the mental grasp.

Nowhere can one see more clearly illustrated what may be called the *sensibility* of such an organic complex, expressed by the fact that whatever affects any species belonging to it must have its influence of some sort upon the whole assemblage. He will thus be made to see the impossibility of studying completely any form out of relation to the other forms; the necessity for taking a comprehensive survey of the whole as a condition to a satisfactory understanding of any part. If one wishes to become acquainted with the black bass, for example, he will learn but little if he limits himself to that species. He must evidently study also the species upon which it depends for its existence, and the various conditions upon which *these* depend. He must likewise study the species with which it comes in competition, and the entire system of conditions affecting their prosperity; and by the time he has studied all these sufficiently he will find that he has run through the whole complicated mechanism of the aquatic life of the locality, both animal and vegetable, of which his species forms but a single element. . . .

It would be quite impossible, within reasonable limits, to go into details respecting the organic relations of the animals of these waters,

Reprinted with the publisher's permission from the Illinois Natural History Survey Bulletin, Vol. 15 (1925), pp. 537-550. A reprint of the article as it first appeared in the Bulletin of the Peoria Scientific Association (1887), pp. 77-87.

and I will content myself with two or three illustrations. As one example of the varied and far-reaching relations into which the animals of a lake are brought in the general struggle for life, I take the common black bass. In the dietary of this fish I find, at different ages of the individual, fishes of great variety, representing all the important orders of that class; insects in considerable number, especially the various water bugs and larvæ of dayflies; fresh-water shrimps; and a great multitude of Entomostraca of many species and genera. The fish is therefore directly dependent upon all these classes for its existence. Next, looking to the food of the species which the bass has eaten, and upon which it is therefore indirectly dependent, I find that one kind of the fishes taken feeds upon mud, algæ, and Entomostraca, and another upon nearly every animal substance in the water, including mollusks and decomposing organic matter.

And now if we search for its competitors we shall find these also extremely numerous. In the first place, I have found that all our young fishes except the Catostomidæ feed at first almost wholly on Entomostraca, so that the little bass finds himself at the very beginning of his life engaged in a scramble for food with all the other little fishes in the lake. In fact, not only young fishes but a multitude of other animals as well, especially insects and the larger Crustacea, feed upon these Entomostraca, so that the competitors of the bass are not confined to members of its own class. Even mollusks, while they do not directly compete with it do so indirectly, for they appropriate myriads of the microscopic forms upon which the Entomostraca largely depend for food. But the enemies of the bass do not all attack it by appropriating its food supplies, for many devour the little fish itself. A great variety of predaceous fishes, turtles, water snakes, wading and diving birds, and even bugs of gigantic dimensions destroy it on the slightest opportunity. It is in fact hardly too much to say that fishes which reach maturity are relatively as rare as centenarians among human kind. . . .

Perhaps no phenomenon of life in such a situation is more remarkable than the steady balance of organic nature, which holds each species within the limits of a uniform average number, year after year, although each one is always doing its best to break across boundaries on every side. The reproductive rate is usually enormous and the struggle for existence is correspondingly severe. . . .

It is a self-evident proposition that a species can not maintain itself continuosly, year after year, unless its birth rate at least equals its death rate. If it is preyed upon by another species, it must produce regularly an excess of individuals for destruction, or else it must certainly dwindle and disappear. On the other hand, the dependent species evidently must not appropriate, on an average, any more than the surplus and excess of individuals upon which it preys, for it it does so it will continuously diminish its own food supply, and thus indirectly but surely exterminate itself. The interests of both parties will therefore be best served by an adjustment of their respective rates of multiplication such that the species devoured shall furnish an excess of numbers to supply the wants of the devourer, and that the latter shall confine its appropriations to the excess thus furnished. We thus see that there is really a close *community of interest* between these two seemingly deadly foes.

And next we note that this common interest is promoted by the process of natural selection; for it is the great office of this process to eliminate the unfit. If two species standing to each other in the relation of hunter and prey are or become badly adjusted in respect to their rates of increase, so that the one preyed upon is kept very far below the normal number which might find food, even if they do not presently obliterate each other the pair are placed at a disadvantage in the battle for life, and must suffer accordingly. Just as certainly as the thrifty businessman who lives within his income will finally dispossess his shiftless competitor who can never pay his debts, the well-adjusted aquatic animal will in time crowd out its poorly-adjusted competitors for food and for the various goods of life. Consequently we may believe that in the long run and as a general rule those species which have survived, are those which have reached a fairly close adjustment in this particular.

Two ideas are thus seen to be sufficient to explain the order evolved from this seeming chaos; the first that of a general community of interests among all the classes of organic beings here assembled, and the second that of the beneficent power if natural selection which compels such adjustments of the rates of destruction and of multiplication of the various species as shall best promote this common interest.

58

the geographic distribution of life in North America

C. HART MERRIAM

No phenomenon in the whole realm of nature forced itself earlier upon the notice of man than certain facts of geographic distribution. The daily search for food, the first and principal occupation of savage man, directed his attention to the unequal distribution of animals and plants. He not only noticed that certain kinds were found in rivers, ponds, or the sea, and others on land, and that some terrestrial kinds were never seen except in forests, while others were as exclusively restricted to open prairies, but he observed further, when his excursions were extended to more distant localities or from the valleys and plains to the summits of neighboring mountains, that unfamiliar fruits and insects and birds and mammals were met with, while those he formerly knew disappeared.

Thus primeval man, and in truth the ancestors of primeval man, learned by observation the great fact of geographic distribution, the fact that particular kinds of animals and plants are not uniformly diffused over the earth, but are restricted to more or less circumscribed areas.

It will be observed that two classes of cases are here referred to, namely, (1) cases in which in the same general region certain species are restricted to swamps or lowlands, while others are confined to dense forests or rocky hillsides – differences of *station,* and (2) cases in which, regardless of *local* pecularities, a general change takes place

Reprinted from the Proceedings of the Biological Society of Washington, Vol. 7 (1892), pp. 1-64.

in the fauna and flora in passing from one region to another, or from low valleys or plains to high mountains – *geographic* differences. The latter class only is here considered. . . .

In passing from the tropics to the Arctic pole on the eastern side of America a number of distant zones are crossed, the most conspicuous features of which are well known. In the plant world the palms, mangroves, mahogany, mastic, Jamaica dogwood, and cassias of the tropical coast districts are succeeded by the magnolias, pawpaws, sweet gums, hackberries, and persimmons of the Southern States. These give place gradually to the oaks, chestnuts, and hickories of the Middle States, and the latter to the groves of aspen, maple, and beech which reach the southern edge of the great coniferous forest of the north – a forest of spruces and firs that stretches completely across the continent from Labrador to Alaska. Beyond this forest is a treeless expanse whose distant shores are bathed in the icy waters of the Arctic Ocean.

Concurrently with these changes in vegetation from the south northward occur equally marked differences in the mammals, birds, reptiles, and insects. Among mammals the tapirs, monkeys, armadillos, nasuas, peccaries, and opossums of Central America and Mexico are replaced to the northward by wood rats, marmots, chipmunks, foxes, rabbits, short-tailed field mice of several genera, shrews, wildcats, lynxes, short-tailed porcupines, elk, moose, reindeer, sables, fishers, wolverines, lemmings, musk oxen, and polar bears.

The trogons, sawbills, parrots, cotingas and other birds of tropical America give place in turn to the cardinals, blue grosbeaks, mocking birds, tufted tits, and gnatcatchers of the Southern States; the chewink, indigo bird, tanager, bluebird, and robin of the Middle and Northern States; the Canada jays, crossbills, white-throated sparrows, and hawk owls of the northern coniferous forests, and the ptarmigans, snowy owls, and snowflakes of the Arctic circle. . . .

It is seen that a number of zoologists and botanists, basing their studies on widely different groups, and as a rule ignorant of the writings of their predecessors, have agreed in the main in the recognition of at least seven (7) life areas in extratropical North America, namely: (1) an *Arctic area* north of the limit of tree growth; (2) a *Boreal transcontinental coniferous forest region;* (3) an *Atlantic or Eastern wooded region* stretching westward from the Atlantic to the Great Plains; (4) a *Central or Middle region,* reaching from the Plains to the Sierra Nevada and Cascade Mountains; (5) a *Pacific or Californian division,* covering the area between the east base of the Sierra and the Pacific Ocean; (6) a Louisianian or *Austroriparian division,* comprising the South Atlantic and Gulf States south of latitude 36°; (7) a *Sonoran division,* occupying the high tableland of Mexico and stretching northward over the dry interior far enough to include the southern parts of California, Nevada, Arizona, New Mexico, and Texas. . . .

It is now pretty generally conceded that temperature and humidity are the chief factors governing the distribution of life, and that temperature is more potent than humidity. Illustrations of this law have been already given in contrasting the humid and arid elements of the several zones with the zone elements as limited by temperature, and it has been found in the case of mammals and birds that the effects of temperature, estimated numerically, are more than three times greater than the effects of humidity upon genera, and many times greater upon the higher groups.

Authors differ as to the exact period during which temperature exerts the greatest influence, but there can be little doubt that for both animals and plants it is *the season of reproductive activity,* and hence varies inversely with latitude and altitude. In high arctic latitudes this period is very brief, while in the humid tropics it seems to extend over nearly if not quite the whole year.

Whether the temperature in question is the mean of a certain period or the sum of the daily temperatures for that period, or the sum in excess of a certain minimum, expressed in degrees of the thermometric scale or in calories, and how to determine the precise beginning and ending of this period for each locality are questions respecting which difference of opinion prevails and authors are not agreed as to whether the temperature should be taken in the sun or in the shade, or at a certain distance below the surface of the earth. At the same time it has been demonstrated by Linsser and others that a definite quantity of heat is required to complete the process of reproduction in a number of plants experimented upon – and nature's laws are not framed for isolated cases. This law is taken advantage of by expert gardeners and horticulturists who are able to so regulate the temperature of their greenhouses that they can produce a perfect flower or a ripe fruit on a specified day.

A few species, particularly among plants, are so sensitive to cold that they are limited in northward range by the line of killing frost, but in the vast majority of cases the winter temperature is of no consequence. As I have already shown, "The season of reproduction for the plant, as for the animal, is the warm part of the year. After the period of reproduction the plant withers; after it flowers and fruits and matures its seed, it dies down or becomes physiologically inactive. And what the plant accomplishes in one way the animal accomplishes in another. To escape the cold of winter and its consequences, the sensitive mammal hibernates; the bird migrates to a more southern latitude; the reptile and batrachian dig holes in the mud or sand and remain in a torpid condition; the insect sleeps in its cocoon or buries itself under leaves or decomposing vegetation; and none but the hardier forms of life are left to be affected by winter temperatures."

After temperature and humidity, several subordinate though important factors remain to be considered. Among these may be mentioned the duration and actinic effects of sunlight (governed in part by percentage of cloudiness or fog and by the mechanical purity of the atmosphere). The character of the soil also determines the presence or absence of many species. . . .

59

climatic and edaphic factors

A. F. W. SCHIMPER

If one looks down upon the flat virgin tract of country from a considerable height, say from the top of a mountain, or better still from a balloon, the character of its vegetation as a rule appears uniform, either as *woodland, grassland,* or *desert.* It is true that even from a great distance some interruptions of the prevailing monotony may be distinguished. Where for instance a river traverses the grassy landscape, its banks are frequently clad by belts of forests, or the dry desert shows spots and strips of luxuriant vegetation. These are indeed mere accidents, having no influence on the general character of the landscape which, excepting where two districts meet, always belongs to one or other of the three above-mentioned types.

Chains of mountains are frequently boundary walls between districts of dissimilar types of vegetation. Thus the forest district of North Africa is separated by the Atlas Mountains from the Sahara desert, that of North Venezuela by the Cordilleras from the grassland of the Llanos, the forest of Brazil and the Argentine by the Andes from the desert of Peru, Bolivia, and North Chili. In other cases the transition is more gradual. The eastern forest district of North America gradually passes westward into the grassland district of the prairies, and the latter towards the west gradually assumes the condition of a desert; a similar phenomenon is exhibited in the transition from the Russian forest dis-

Reprinted with the publisher's permission from Plant geography upon a physiolcgical basis, translated by W. R. Fisher, revised and edited by Percy Groom and Isaac B. Balfour. Clarendon Press, Oxford (1903).

trict to the South Russian steppes, and from the latter to the Caspian desert. Whether the change be more sudden or more gradual, it always corresponds to a change in climatic humidity.

The type of vegetation in the tropical and temperate zones is determined by the amount and distribution of the rainfall, by the humidity of the air, and by the movements of the atmosphere, which essentially affect vegetation only by their desiccating influence.

The type of the flora in so far as it depends on existing factors is dependent primarily on heat, especially if we consider, not the groups of lower order (genera and species), but those of higher order (cohorts, orders, and families). Only in polar areas is the temperature important as a climatic cause of a type of vegetation – in the cold desert or tundra.

On nearer approach the uniform character of the vegetation of a district appears much less distinct, for to the irregularities already visible from a distance a number of fresh ones are added, such as small patches covered with reeds in the midst of a forest, scantily stocked gravel, and the like. Moreover, woodland, grassland, and desert display many fine shades of differences within their types; here the character is more hygrophilous, there more xerophilous, with countless stages between the two extremes. Finally, the composition of the flora that could in most cases not be discerned from a distance is subject to more or less sudden changes. This fine differentiation of the vegetation and flora within a climatic district is chiefly determined by the soil. Only when there is considerable unevenness of surface does the inequality of the insolation operate as well; but the influence of this factor is always subordinate to the physical and chemical nature of the soil.

The differentiation of the earth's vegetation is thus controlled by three factors – heat, atmospheric precipitation (including winds), soil. Heat determines the flora, climatic humidity the vegetation; the soil as a rule merely picks out and blends the material supplied by these two climatic factors, and on its own account adds a few details.

The blending activity of the soil leads to a differentiation into sometimes smaller and sometimes larger groups of uniform oecological and floristic type, the characteristics of which are exactly repeated on the same kinds of soil so long as the climate is unchanged, whereas the different kinds of soil bear different kinds of plants. *The communities of plants as determined by the qualities of the soil are termed formations.*

In each formation one species of plant, or a group of species, is characteristic; plants that merely occur sporadically are unessential to the formation, and commoner subsidiary constituents can only give a different facies to the formation. Thus, in Europe, we are acquainted with the formation of the beech-forest, where Fagus sylvatica predominates, and with at least two facies of dissimilar herbaceous vegetation. If the composition of the vegetation should alter while the nature of the soil remains unchanged, this is a certain indication of transition into another climate. A sudden change of formations while the quality of the soil remains unaltered is only found in mountain ranges in relation to the sudden change in climate.

Whilst every formation is in its floristic and oecological character a product of climate and soil, yet the influence of the several climatic and edaphic factors is not equal. The influence of the soil is always subordinate to that of the climatic temperature, whereas under certain conditions that are indeed merely local it neutralizes that of the atmospheric precipitation. Thus woods occur in many spots where the climate would give rise to grassland, or we may find the converse, and vigorous forest thrives in patches under a desert climate with a very scanty atmospheric precipitation. Definite properties of the soil may also bring forth a character of vegetation that belongs to none of the climatic types. These climatic types demand a favourable constitution of the soil congenial to the vast majority of the plants. Extreme properties of the soil that are unfavourable to the life of most plants set vegetation free from the controlling influence of atmospheric precipitation. Consequently the vegetation of rocks, gravel, swamps, and other special spots, bears in the highest degree the oecological impress of the substratum, and this impress for the most part remains identical under very dissimilar conditions of climatic humidity, which on such soils plays only a subordinate part.

From what has preceded it appears that *two oecological groups of formations* should be distinguished – the *climatic or district formations*, the character of whose vegetation is governed by atmospheric precipitations, and the *edaphic or local formations*, whose vegetation is chiefly determined by the nature of the soil. . . .

60

floristic and ecological plant-geography; ecological classification

EUGENE WARMING

Plant-geography deals with the distribution of plants upon the earth, and with the principles determining this. We may regard this distribution from two different standpoints, and accordingly may divide the subject into two branches, *floristic plant-geography* and *oecological plant-geography;* but these are merely different aspects of the same science, touching at many points and occasionally merging into one another.

Floristic plant-geography is concerned with –

1. The compilation of a "Flora," that is, a list of species growing within a larger or smaller area. . . .

2. The division of the earth's surface into natural floristic tracts. . . according to their affinities. . . .

3. The subdivision of the larger natural floristic tracts . . . and the precise definition of these.

4. The discussion of the limits of distribution of species, genera, and families. . . .

The thoughtful investigator will not remain content with the mere recognition of facts; he will seek after their *causes.* These are, in part, *modern* (geognostic, topographical, and climatic), and, in part, *historical.* . . .

Reprinted with the publisher's permission from Œcology of plants, an introduction to the study of plant communities, translated by Percy Groom and Isaac Balfour, Clarendon Press, Oxford (1909).

Oecological plant-geography has entirely different objects in view:—

It teaches us how plants or plant-communities adjust their forms and modes of behaviour to actually operating factors, such as the amounts of available water, heat, light, nutriment, and so forth.

A casual glance shows that species by no means dispose their individuals uniformly over the whole area in which they occur, but group them into communities of very varied physiognomy. Oecology seeks —

1. To find out which species are commonly associated together upon similar habitats (stations). . . .
2. To sketch the physiognomy of the vegetation and the landscape.
3. To answer the questions —

   Why each species has its own special habit and habitat,
   Why the species congregate to form definite communities,
   Why these have a characteristic physiognomy. . . .
4. To investigate the problems concerning the economy of plants, the demands that they make on their environment, and the means that they employ to utilize the surrounding conditions and to adapt their external and internal structure and general form for that purpose. We thus come to the consideration of the *growth-forms* of plants. . . .

The foregoing chapters have made it clear that the distinctions between water plants and land plants are deep-seated, and concern the external form as well as the internal structure. Plant-communities must therefore be grouped in the first place into aquatic and terrestrial; but between these there is no sharp boundary, for there is a group of plants, marsh plants (*helophytes*), which, like water plants, develop their lower parts (roots, rhizomes, and, to some extent, leaves) in water or at least in soaking soil, but have their assimilatory organs mainly adapted to existence in air, as is the case with land plants to which they are closely allied. Helophytes give rise to special forms of communities. Yet we must include among water plants all those plants that, like Nymphaeaceae, approximate to land plants in so far as they have floating leaves, which are more or less adapted to existence in air, but are nevertheless mainly designed for existence upon water.

It has already been shown that land plants exhibit many grades of adaptation to their mode of life in contact with air, and that those which encounter the greatest difficulties in regard to securing water are termed *xerophytes;* while others are described as *mesophytes* because in some respects they stand midway between the two extremes, hydrophytes and xerophytes. The differentiation of the land plant in one or the other direction is decided by the oecological factors, edaphic and climatic, that prevail in the *station* or *habitat.* But edaphic and climatic factors cannot be regarded separately: the plant-community is always the product of both together. The nature of a soil is also influenced by climate, and it is incontestible that climate (rainfall) calls forth the wide differences between, say, desert and tropical rain-forest. But it is far from being true that climate alone calls into existence the different communities of plants which will hereafter be defined as *formations*. Characters of the soil are of supreme importance in determining the production of formations, and they must therefore be the foundation of oecological classification. Clements, with reason, has objected to Schimper's scheme of distinguishing between climatic and edaphic formations, if indeed it was Schimper's meaning that a sharp distinction is throughout possible, and that both groups of factors are of equal potency. . . .

When endeavouring to arrange all land plants, omitting marsh plants, into comprehensive groups, we meet with, first, some communities that are evidently influenced in the main by the physical and chemical characters of soil which determine the amount of water therein; secondly, other communities in which extreme climatic conditions and fluctuations, seasonal distribution of rain, and the like, decide the amount of water in soil and character of vegetation. In accordance with these facts, land plants may be ranged into groups, though in a very uncertain manner. The prevailing vagueness in this grouping *is* due to the fact *that oecology is only in its infancy,* and that *very few* detailed investigations of plant-communities have been conducted, the published descriptions of vegetation being nearly always one-sided and floristic, as well as very incomplete and unsatisfactory from an oecological standpoint. . . .

61

the relation of physiological characters to geographic range

VICTOR E. SHELFORD

Our studies of animal distribution usually consist of a list of names of species with a statement of the distribution of each, followed by such interpretation as suits our particular purposes. Attempts actually to study the environment in any detail, or the reactions of animals to the conditions of environment are rare indeed. Furthermore, the groups most studied (higher vertebrates) are probably least dependent upon their environmental complexes; they are often decidedly migratory and because of their size least adapted to experimental study.

Some quite extensive attempts to correlate geographic range with meteorological conditions have been made but always with only implied reference to the physiological character of the organisms themselves, and usually with the use of *species* as an *index of conditions*. A few factors have been emphasized, and these usually in the sense of barriers. Merriam emphasizes temperature; Walker atmospheric moisture. Heilprin, like most paleontologists, emphasizes food. There appears to be no adequate basis for the idea that the same single factor governs the distribution of most animals. Such a conclusion probably results from leaving the organism out of consideration.

Since the environment is a complex of many factors, every animal lives surrounded by and responds to a complex of factors, at least in its normal life activities within its normal complex. Can a single factor control distribution?

Reprinted with the author's and publisher's permission from Physiological animal geography. Journal of Morphology, Vol. 22 (1911), pp. 551-618.

A large amount of physiological study of organisms has been conducted with particular reference to the analysis of the organism itself, but with little reference to natural environments. Many of the factors and conditions employed in such experiments are of such a nature that the animal never or rarely encounters them in its regular normal life. Other experiments are, however, attempts to keep the environment normal, except for one factor. These have demonstrated that in ordinary reactions an animal responds to the action of a single stimulus. Certain general laws govern the reaction of animals to different intensities of the same stimulus.

a. Laws governing the reactions of animals. The laws governing the stimulation of animals in the experiments of the laboratory are familiar subjects in the textbooks of physiology. With respect to a given factor used in the experiment, it has been found that there is a range of conditions within which the activities of the animal proceed without marked stimulative features. These are called optimal conditions. Take, for example, temperature. There is in most animals, which have been subjected to experimentation with temperature, a range of several degrees in which the animal is not markedly stimulated (optimum). As the temperature is raised or lowered from such a condition, the animal is stimulated. If the temperature be continuously raised, a point is reached at which the animal dies. The temperature condition just before death occurs is called the maximum. The lowering of temperature produces results comparable in a general way to those of high temperature. The condition just before the death point is reached is called the minimum. With various limitations, unimportant in this connection, the same is true with respect to each of the various factors which an animal encounters in nature. Which factor determines the limitations of occurrence of an animal on the earth's surface? The answer to this is suggested in Liebig's Law of Minimum.

b. Law of minimum. Liebig's law of minimum is summarized by Johnstone:

A plant requires a certain number of foodstuffs if it is to continue to live and grow. Each of these food substances must be present in a certain proportion. If it is absent the plant will die; if present in a minimal proportion the growth will also be minimal. This is true no matter how abundant the other foodstuffs may be. The growth is then dependent upon the amount of foodstuff present in minimal quantity.

In nature this law applies both geographically and locally. As applied to animals it includes both food and material for abode. The presence, absence and success of a species is determined by the necessary material which is absent or present in minimal quantity.

c. Law of toleration of physical factors. We have noted in the case of the tiger beetles, that for the egg-laying to take place the surrounding temperature and light must both be suitable, the soil must be moist, probably also warm, and must satify the ovipositor tests with respect to several factors. Egg-laying, the *positive reaction,* is then probably a response to several factors. Furthermore, after the eggs are laid, the conditions favorable for egg-laying must continue for about two weeks if the eggs are to hatch and the larvæ reach the surface of the ground. The success of reproduction depends, then, upon the qualitative and quantitative *completeness* of the complex of conditions. The *negative reaction,* on the other hand, appears to be different. The absence of eggs, the number of failures to lay and therefore the number of eggs laid in any situation can be controlled by qualitative or quantitative deficiency or excess with respect to *any one of several factors.* The presence, absence, or number of eggs laid is, then, determinable by a single factor, according as it is near the optimum or near either the maximum or minimum tolerated by the species. It is, however, not necessary that a single factor deviate; the effect is similar or more pronounced if several deviate.

In nature the presence or absence, or success of a species or group of species, its numbers and sometimes its size, etc. are largely determined by the degree of deviation of a factor or factors from the range of optimum of the species or group of species. The cause of the deviation in the factor or factors is not of importance. For example, in the case of a soil inhabiting species such as Cicindela tranquebarica, to which considerable moisture is necessary, the cause of the deficiency in one case may be climatic deficiency in rainfall, in another a rapid drainage due to steep slope and porosity of soil. The former is what we have called a climatic (geographic) condition and the latter a local condition. The evidence for the law of toleration as applying to distribution is good so far as the local distribution is concerned and, since the same factors are involved in the geographic, there is no difficulty in the application of the law to geographic distribution also. The fact that in so far as our observation can go at present, the tiger beetles are found in similar conditions throughout their ranges, is also good evidence for the application of both the laws of minimum and toleration to geographic distribution. In fact the *law of minimum* is but a special case of the *law of toleration.* Combinations of the factors which fall under the law of minimum may be made, which makes the law of toleration apply quite generally; for example: food and excretory products may be taken together as constituting a single factor. From this point of view the law of toleration applies, the food acting on the minimum side, excretory products on the maximum.

d. Application of the law of toleration to geographic distribution. The so-called centers of distribution are often only areas in which conditions are optimum for a considerable number of species. The relation of the law to centers of distribution is shown in the diagram below; above the line is the scale of stimulation with the limits of toleration shown and below the parallel relation of the distribution and relative abundance.

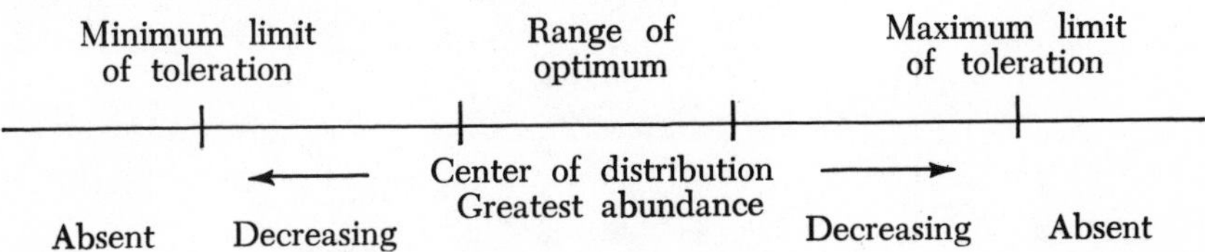

On account of the nature and distribution of climatic and vegetation conditions, it follows that as we pass in one direction from a center, one factor may fluctuate beyond the range of toleration of a species under consideration; but as we pass in another direction it is very likely to be a *different* factor. The divisions of Merriam's zones into arid and humid portions is an illustration of this, and seems to constitute a begging of the temperature question. . . .

62

food chains; niches; and the pyramid of numbers

CHARLES ELTON

Animals are not always struggling for existence, but when they do begin, they spend the greater part of their lives eating. Feeding is such a universal and commonplace business that we are inclined to forget its importance. The primary driving force of all animals is the necessity of finding the right kind of food and enough of it. Food is the burning question in animal society, and the whole structure and activities of the community are dependent upon questions of food supply. We are not concerned here with the various devices employed by animals to enable them to obtain their food, or with the physiological processes which enable them to utilise in their tissues the energy derived from it. It is sufficient to bear in mind that animals have to depend ultimately upon plants for their supplies of energy, since plants alone are able to turn raw sunlight and chemicals into a form edible to animals. Consequently herbivores are the basic class in animal society. Another difference between animals and plants is that while plants are all competing for much the same class of food, animals have the most varied diets, and there is a great divergence in their food habits. The herbivores are usually preyed upon by carnivores, which get the energy of the sunlight at third-hand, and these again may be preyed upon by other carnivores, and so on, until we reach an animal which has no enemies, and which forms, as it were, a terminus on this food cycle. There are, in fact, chains of animals linked together by food, and all dependent in the long run

Reprinted with the author's and publisher's permission from Animal ecology. Sidgwick and Jackson, Ltd., London (1927).

upon plants. We refer to these as "food chains," and to all the food chains in a community as the "food cycle."

8. Starting from herbivorous animals of various sizes, there are as a rule a number of food chains radiating outwards, in which the carnivores become larger and larger, while the parasites are smaller than their hosts. . . . In the sea, diatoms form the basic plant food, and there are a number of crustacea (chiefly copepods) which turn these algae into food which can be eaten by larger animals. Copepods are living winnowing fans, and they form what may be called a "key industry" in the sea. The term "key industry" is a useful one, and is used to denote animals which feed upon plants and which are so numerous as to have a very large number of animals dependent upon them. This point is considered again in the section on "Niches." . . .

At whatever animal community we look, we find that it is organised in a similar way. Sometimes plants are not the immediate basis of the food cycle. This is the case with scavengers, and with such associations as the fauna of temporary fresh-water pools and of the abyssal parts of the sea where the immediate basic food is mud and detritus; and the same is true of many parasitic faunas. In all these cases, which are peculiar, the food supply is of course ultimately derived from plants, but owing to the isolation of the animals it is convenient to treat them as a separate community. . . .

15. It should be pretty clear by now that although the actual species of animals are different in different habitats, the ground plan of every animal community is much the same. In every community we should find herbivorous and carnivorous and scavenging animals. We can go further than this, however: in every kind of wood in England we should find some species of aphid, preyed upon by some species of ladybird. Many of the latter live exclusively on aphids. That is why they make such good controllers of aphid plagues in orchards. When they have eaten all the pest insects they just die of starvation, instead of turning their attention to some other species of animal, as so many carnivores do under similar circumstances. There are many animals which have equally well-defined food habits. A fox carries on the very definite business of killing and eating rabbits and mice and some kinds of birds. The beetles of the genus *Stenus* pursue and catch springtails (*Collembola*) by means of their extensile tongues. Lions feed on large ungulates – in many places almost entirely zebras. Instances could be multiplied indefinitely. It is therefore convenient to have some term to describe the status of an animal in its community, to indicate what it is *doing* and not merely what it looks like, and the term used is "niche." Animals have all manner of external factors acting upon them – chemical, physi-

cal, and biotic — and the "niche" of an animal means its place in the biotic environment, *its relations to food and enemies.* The ecologist should cultivate the habit of looking at animals from this point of view as well as from the ordinary standpoints of appearance, names, affinities, and past history. When an ecologist says "there goes a badger" he should include in his thoughts some definite idea of the animal's place in the community to which it belongs, just as if he had said "there goes the vicar."

16. The niche of an animal can be defined to a large extent by its size and food habits. We have already referred to the various key-industry animals which exist, and we have used the term to denote herbivorous animals which are sufficiently numerous to support a series of carnivores. There is in every typical community a series of herbivores ranging from small ones (*e.g.* aphids) to large ones (*e.g.* deer). Within the herbivores of any one size there may be further differentiation according to food habits. Special niches are more easily distinguished among carnivores, and some instances have already been given. . . .

21. "One hill cannot shelter two tigers." In other and less interesting words, many carnivorous animals, especially at or near the end of a food chain, have some system of territories, whereby it is arranged that each individual, or pair, or family, has an area of country sufficiently large to supply its food requirements. Hawks divide up the country in this way, and Eliot Howard's work has shown that similar territory systems play a very important part in the lives of warblers. We can approach the matter also from this point of view: the smaller an animal the commoner it is on the whole. This is familiar enough as a general fact. If you are studying the fauna of an oak wood in summer, you will find vast numbers of small herbivorous insects like aphids, a large number of spiders and carnivorous ground beetles, a fair number of small warblers, and only one or two hawks. Similarly in a small pond, the numbers of protozoa may run into millions, those of *Daphnia* and *Cyclops* into hundreds of thousands, while there will be far fewer beetle larvæ, and only a very few small fish. To put the matter more definitely, the animals at the base of a food chain are relatively abundant, while those at the end are relatively few in numbers, and there is a progressive decrease in between the two extremes. The reason for this fact is simple enough. The small herbivorous animals which form the key industries in the community are able to increase at a very high rate (chiefly by virtue of their small size), and are therefore able to provide a large margin of numbers over and above that which would be necessary to maintain their population in the absence of enemies. This margin supports a set of carnivores, which are larger in size and fewer in numbers.

These carnivores in turn can only provide a still smaller margin, owing to their large size which makes them increase more slowly, and to their smaller numbers. Finally, a point is reached at which we find a carnivore (*e.g.* the lynx or the peregrine falcon) whose numbers are so small that it cannot support any further stage in the food chain. There is obviously a lower limit in the density of numbers of its food at which it ceases to be worth while for a carnivore to eat that food, owing to the labour and time that is involved in the process. It is because of these number relations that carnivores tend to be much more wide-ranging and less strictly confined to one habitat than herbivores.

22. This arrangement of numbers in the community, the relative decrease in numbers at each stage in a food chain, is characteristically found in animal communities all over the world, and to it we have applied the term "pyramid of numbers." It results, as we have seen, from the two facts *(a)* that smaller animals are preyed upon usually by larger animals, and (*b*) that small animals can increase faster than large ones, and so are able to support the latter. . . .

63

the trophic-dynamic aspect of ecology

RAYMOND L. LINDEMAN

The trophic-dynamic viewpoint, as adopted in this paper, emphasizes the relationship of trophic or "energy-availing" relationships within the community-unit to the process of succession. . . . Upon further consideration of the trophic cycle, the discrimination between living organisms as parts of the "biotic community" and dead organisms and inorganic nutritives as parts of the "environment" seems arbitrary and unnatural. The difficulty of drawing clear-cut lines between the living *community* and the non-living *environment* is illustrated by the difficulty of determining the status of a slowly dying pondweed covered with periphytes, some of which are also continually dying. . . . much of the non-living nascent ooze is rapidly reincorporated through "dissolved nutrients" back into the living "biotic community." This constant organic-inorganic cycle of nutritive substance is so completely integrated that to consider even such a unit as a lake primarily as a biotic community appears to force a "biological" emphasis upon a more basic functional organization. . . .

TROPHIC DYNAMICS

Qualitative food-cycle relationships. Although certain aspects of food relations have been known for centuries, many processes within ecosystems are still very incompletely understood. The basic process in trophic dynamics is the transfer of energy from one part of the eco-

Reprinted with the publisher's permission from Ecology, Vol. 23 (1942), pp. 399-418

system to another. All function, and indeed all life, within an ecosystem depends upon the utilization of an external source of energy, solar radiation. A portion of this incident energy is transformed by the process of photosynthesis into the structure of living organisms. In the language of community economics introduced by Thienemann, autotrophic plants are *producer* organisms, employing the energy obtained by photosynthesis to synthesize complex organic substances from simple inorganic substances. Although plants again release a portion of this potential energy in catabolic processes, a great surplus of organic substance is accumulated. Animals and heterotrophic plants, as *consumer* organisms, feed upon this surplus of potential energy, oxidizing a considerable portion of the consumed substance to release kinetic energy for metabolism, but transforming the remainder into the complex chemical substances of their own bodies. Following death, every organism is a potential source of energy for saprophagous organisms (feeding directly on dead tissues), which again may act as energy sources for successive categories of consumers. Heterotrophic bacteria and fungi, representing the most important saprophagous consumption of energy, may be conveniently differentiated from animal consumers as specialized *decomposers* of organic substance. Waksman has suggested that certain of these bacteria be further differentiated as *transformers* of organic and inorganic compounds. The combined action of animal consumers and bacterial decomposers tends to dissipate the potential energy of organic substances, again transforming them to the inorganic state. From this inorganic state the autotrophic plants may utilize the dissolved nutrients once more in resynthesizing complex organic substance, thus completing the food cycle. . . .

Productivity. DEFINITIONS. The quantitative aspects of trophic ecology have been commonly expressed in terms of the productivity of the food groups concerned. Productivity has been rather broadly defined as the general rate of production, a term which may be applied to any or every food group in a given ecosystem. . . .

Biological efficiency. The quantitative relationships of any food-cycle level may be expressed in terms of its efficiency with respect to lower levels. Quoting Hutchinson's definition, "the efficiency of the productivity of any level (Λ_n) relative to the productivity of any previous level (Λ_m) is defined as (λ_n/λ_m) 100. If the rate of solar energy entering the ecosystem is denoted as λ_o, the efficiencies of all levels may be referred back to this quantity λ_o." In general, however, the most interesting efficiencies are those referred to the previous level's productivity (λ_{n-1}), or those expressed as $(\lambda_n/\lambda_{n-1})$ 100. These latter may be termed the *progressive efficiencies* of the various food-cycle levels, indicating for each level the degree of utilization of its potential food supply or energy source. All efficiencies discussed in the following pages are progressive efficiencies, expressed in terms of relative productivities $((\lambda_n/\lambda_{n-1})\ 100)$. It is important to remember that efficiency and productivity are not synonymous. Productivity is a rate (i.e., in the units here used, cal/cm^2/year), while efficiency, being a ratio, is a dimensionless number. The points of reference for any efficiency value should always be clearly stated.

The progressive efficiencies $((\lambda_n/\lambda_{n-1})\ 100)$ for the trophic levels of Cedar Bog Lake and Lake Mendota, as obtained from the productivities derived in tables 2 and 3, are presented in table 4. In view of the

TABLE 4. Productivities and progressive efficiencies in the Cedar Bog Lake and Lake Mendota food cycles, as g-cal/cm^2/year

	Cedar Bog Lake		Lake Mendota	
	Productivity	Efficiency	Productivity	Efficiency
Radiation	≦118,872		118,872	
Producers: Λ_1	111.3	0.10%	480*	0.40%
Primary consumers: Λ_2	14.8	13.3%	41.6	8.7%
Secondary consumers: Λ_3	3.1	22.3%	2.3†	5.5%
Tertiary consumers: Λ_4			0.3	13.0%

*Probably too high; see footnote of table 3.
†Probably too low; see footnote of table 3.

uncertainties concerning some of the Lake Mendota productivities, no definite conclusions can be drawn from their relative efficiencies. The Cedar Bog Lake ratios, however, indicate that the progressive efficiencies increase from about 0.10 per cent for production to 13.3 per cent for primary consumption and to 22.3 per cent for secondary consumption. . . . These progressively increasing efficiencies may well represent a fundamental trophic principle, namely, that the consumers at progressively higher levels in the food cycle are progressively more efficient in the use of their food supply.

At first sight, this generalization of increasing efficiency in higher consumer groups would appear to contradict the previous generalization that the loss of energy due to respiration is progressively greater for higher levels in the food cycle. These can be reconciled by remembering that increased activity of predators considerably increases the chances of encountering suitable prey. The ultimate effect of such antagonistic principles would present a picture of a predator completely wearing itself out in the process of completely exterminating its prey, a very improbable situation. However, Elton pointed out that food cycles rarely have more than five trophic levels. Among the several factors involved, increasing respiration of successive levels of predators contrasted with their successively increasing efficiency of predation appears to be important in restricting the number of trophic levels in a food cycle. . . .

TROPHIC-DYNAMICS IN SUCCESSION

Dynamic processes within an ecosystem, over a period of time, tend to produce certain obvious changes in its species-composition, soil characteristics and productivity. Change, according to Cooper, is the essential criterion of succession. From the trophic-dynamic viewpoint, succession is the process of development in an ecosystem, brought about primarily by the effects of the organisms on the environment and upon each other, towards a relatively stable condition of equilibrium.

It is well known that in the initial phases of hydrarch succession (oligotrophy→eutrophy) productivity increases rapidly; it is equally apparent that the colonization of a bare terrestrial area represents a similar acceleration in productivity. In the later phases of succession, productivity increases much more slowly. . . .

Efficiency relationships in succession. The successional changes of photosynthetic efficiency in natural areas (with respect to solar radiation, i.e., $((\lambda_1/\lambda_n)\ 100)$ have not been intensively studied. In lake succession, photosynthetic efficiency would be expected to follow the same course deduced for productivity, rising to a more or less constant value during eutrophic stage-equilibrium, and declining during senescence, as suggested by a photosynthetic efficiency of at least 0.27 per cent for eutrophic Lake Mendota and of 0.10 per cent for senescent Cedar Bog Lake. For the terrestrial hydrosere, efficiency would likewise follow a curve similar to that postulated for productivity. . . .

64

on living in the biosphere

G. E. HUTCHINSON

The material requirements of life are extremely varied. Between thirty and forty chemical elements appear to be normally involved. Industrially, some use appears to be found for nearly all the natural elements, and some of the new synthetic ones also. Looking at man from a strictly geochemical standpoint, his most striking character is that he demands so much – not merely thirty or forty elements for physiological activity, but nearly all the others for cultural activity. What we may call the anthropogeochemistry of cultural life is worth examining. We find man scurrying about the planet looking for places where certain substances are abundant; then removing them elsewhere, often producing local artificial concentrations far greater than are known in nature. Such concentrations, whether a cube of sodium in a bottle in the laboratory, or the George Washington Bridge, have usually been brought into being by chemical changes, most frequently reductions, of such a kind that the product is unstable under the conditions in which accumulation takes place. Most artifacts are made to be used, and during use the strains to which they are submitted distort them, and they become worn out or broken. This results in a very great quantity of the materials that are laboriously collected being lost again in city dumps and automobile cemeteries. The final fate of an object may depend on many factors, but it is probable that in most cases a very large quantity of any noncombustible, useful material is fated to be carried, either in

Reprinted with the author's and publisher's permission from the Scientific Monthly, Vol. 67 (1948), pp. 393-398.

solution or as sediment, into the sea. Modern man, then, is a very effective agent of zoogenous erosion, but the erosion is highly specific, affecting most powerfully arable soils, forests, accessible mineral deposits, and other parts of the biosphere which provide the things that *Homo sapiens* as a mammal and as an educatable social organism needs or thinks he needs. The process is continuously increasing in intensity, as populations expand and as the most easily eroded loci have added their quotas to the air, the garbage can, the city dump, and the sea.

The most important general consideration to bear in mind in discussing the dynamics of the biosphere and its inhabitants is that some of the processes of significance are acyclical, and others, to a greater or less degree, cyclical. By an acyclical process will be meant one in which a permanent change in geochemical distribution is introduced into the system; usually a concentrated element tends to become dispersed. By a cyclical process will be meant one in which the changes involved introduce no permanent alteration in the large-scale geochemical pattern, concentration alternating with dispersion. The cyclical processes are not necessarily reversible in a thermodynamic sense; in fact, they are in general no more and no less reversible than the acyclical. Most of the cyclical processes operate because a continuous supply of solar energy is led into them, and sunlight will provide no problems for the conservationist for a very long time. It is important to realize that most of the acyclical processes are so slow that man appears as an active intruder into a passive pattern of distribution. They are safer to disturb because we know what the result of the disturbance will be. If we mine the copper in a given region sufficiently assiduously, we know that ultimately there will not be any more copper available there. Cyclical processes involve complex circular paths, regenerative circuits, feedback mechanisms, and the like. Small disturbances of such processes may merely result in small temporary changes, with a rapid return to the previous steady state. . . .

The most nearly perfect cyclical processes are those involving water and nitrogen. Some losses to the sediments of the deep oceanic basins must occur, but they are very small and are doubtless fully balanced or more than balanced by juvenile water and perhaps by molecular nitrogen and ammonia of volcanic origin.

The least cyclical processes are those in which material is removed from the continents and deposited in the permanent basins of the ocean. With one or two exceptions, the delivery to the deep water sediments of the ocean is of little significance. Most of the mechanical and chemical sedimentation in the oceans takes place in relatively shallow water. The uplifting of shallow water sediments constitutes an important method of completing cycles. . . .

The only other cycle that can be considered in any great detail is that of phosphorus. The chief event in the geochemical cycle of phosphorus is the leaching of the element from the rocks of the continents, and its transport by rivers to the sea. At the present time the rate of this transportation is of the order of 20,000,000 tons of phosphorus per year for the entire earth. Part of this phosphorus, when it enters the sea, will ultimately be deposited in the sediments of the depths of the ocean. Such phosphorus will probably be largely lost to the geochemical cycle, as has just been indicated. The sedimentary rocks of the continents, therefore, will gradually lose phosphorus; there is some evidence that this has actually occurred. The main return path is by the uplifting of sediments formed in continental seas, which then undergo renewed chemical erosion. Of particular interest are methods by which concentrated phosphorus can be returned to the land surfaces. As far as is known, there are two such methods: The first is the formation of phosphatic nodules and other forms of phosphate rock in regions of upwelling in which water at a low *p*H, rich in phosphate, is brought up to the surface of the sea. The *p*H falls and an apatite-like phosphate is deposited. When the sea floor is later elevated, a commercial deposit may result. The second method is by the activity of sea birds, such as the guano birds of the Peruvian coast. . . . This process is as characteristic of the time as is glaciation, though less grandiose. Its meaning is not clear, but it is probably connected with changes in vertical circulation of the ocean as glaciopluvial periods gave place to interpluvials. Today in certain regions massive amounts of guano are deposited, and it is probable that the oceanic birds of the world as a whole bring out from several tens to several hundreds of thousands of tons of phosphorus and deposit it on land. Only about 10,000 tons of the element are delivered in places where it is not washed away and where it can be carried by man to fertilize his fields.

The main processes that tend to reverse the phosphorus depletion of the continents are, therefore, the deposition of marine phosphorites on the continental shelves and subsequent elevation, and the formation of guano deposits. Both processes are evidently intermittent, and are quantitatively inadequate to arrest deflection of the element into the permanent ocean basins. Man contributes both to the loss and to the gain of phosphorus by land surfaces. He quarries phosphorite, makes superphosphate of it, and spreads it on his fields. Most of the phosphorus so laboriously acquired ultimately reaches the sea. At present the world's production of phosphate rock is about 10,000,000 tons per annum. This contains from 1,000,000 to 2,000,000 tons of elementary phosphorus. Human activity probably, therefore, accounts for from 5 to 10 percent of the loss of phosphorus from the land to the sea. Man also contributes to the processes bringing phosphorus from the sea to the land. This is done by fisheries. The total catch for the marine fisheries of the earth is of the order of $25–30.10^6$ tons of fish, which corresponds to about 60,000 tons of elementary phosphorus. The human, no less than the non-human, processes tending to complete the cycle seem miserably inadequate. It is quite certain that ultimately man, if he is to avoid famine, will have to go about completing the phosphorus cycle on a large scale. It will be a harder task than that of solving the nitrogen problem, which would have loomed large in any symposium on "The World's Natural Resources" fifty years ago, but possibly an easier problem than some of the others that must be solved if we are to survive and really become the glory of the earth. . . .

65

relationships between structure and function in ecosystems

EUGENE P. ODUM

. . . As you know ecology is often defined as: The study of interrelationships between organisms and environment. I feel that this conventional definition is not suitable; it is too vague and too broad. Personally, I prefer to define ecology as: The study of the structure and function of ecosystems. Or we might say in a less technical way: The study of structure and function of nature.

By structure we mean: (1) The composition of the biological community including species, numbers, biomass, life history and distribution in space of populations; (2) the quantity and distribution of the abiotic (nonliving) materials such as nutrients, water, etc.; (3) the range, or gradient, of conditions of existence such as temperature, light, etc. Dividing ecological structure into these three divisions is, of course, arbitrary but I believe convenient for actual study of both aquatic and terrestrial situations.

By function we mean: (1) The rate of biological energy flow through the ecosystem, that is, the rates of production and the rates of respiration of the populations and the community; (2) the rate of material or nutrient cycling, that is, the biogeochemical cycles; (3) biological or ecological regulation including both regulation of organisms by environment (as, for example, in photoperiodism) and regulation of environment by organisms (as, for example, in nitrogen fixation by

Reprinted with the author's and publisher's permission from the Japanese Journal of Ecology, Vol. 12 (1962), pp. 108-118.

microorganisms). Again, dividing ecological function into these three divisions is arbitrary but convenient for study. . . .

Both aquatic and terrestrial community types have several structural features in common. Both must have the same three necessary biological components: (1) Producers or green plants capable of fixing light energy (i.e., autotrophs); (2) animals or macroconsumers which consume particulate organic matter (i.e., phagotrophs); and (3) microorganism decomposers which dissolve organic matter releasing nutrients (i.e., osmotrophs). Both ecosystems must be supplied with the same vital materials such as nitrogen, phosphorus, trace minerals, etc. Both ecosystems are regulated and limited by the same conditions of existence such as light and temperature. Finally, the arrangement of biological units in vertical space is basically the same in the two contrasting types of ecosystems. Both have two strata, an autotrophic stratum above and a heterotrophic stratum below. The photosynthetic machinery is concentrated in the upper stratum or photic zone where light is available, while the consumer-nutrient regenerating machinery is concentrated largely below the photic zone. It is important to emphasize that while the vertical extent or thickness of communities varies greatly (especially in water), light energy comes into the ecosystem on a horizontal surface basis which is everywhere the same. Thus, different ecosystems should be compared on a square meter basis, not on a cubic or volume basis.

On the other hand, aquatic and terrestrial ecosystems differ in structure in several important ways. Species composition is, of course, completely different; the roles of producers, consumers and decomposers are carried out by taxonomically different organisms which have become adapted through evolution. Trophic structure also differs in that land plants tend to be large in size but few in number while the autotrophs of open water ecosystems (i.e., phytoplankton) are small in size but very numerous. In general, autotrophic biomass is much greater than heterotrophic biomass on land, while the reverse is often true in the sea. Perhaps the most important difference is the following: The matrix, or supporting framework, of the community is largely physical in aquatic ecosystems, but more strongly biological on land. That is to say, the community itself is important as a habitat on land, but not so important in water.

Now, we may ask: How do these similarities and differences in structure affect ecological function?

One important aspect of function is . . . the energy flow through the ecosystems beginning with the incoming solar energy and passing through the successive trophic levels. At each transfer a large part of the energy is dissipated in respiration and passes out of the system as heat. The amount of energy remaining after three steps is so small that it can be ignored in so far as the energetics of the community are concerned. However, tertiary consumers ("top carnivores") can be important as regulators; that is, predation may have an important effect on energy flow at the herbivore level. . . .

The autotrophic-heterotrophic stratification, which we emphasized as a universal feature of community structure, results in two basic food chains. . . . The consumption of living plants by herbivores which live in the autotrophic stratum together with their predators may be considered as the *grazing food chain.* This is the classical food chain of ecology, as, for example, the phytoplankton-zooplankton-fish sequence of the grass-rabbit-fox sequence. However, a large proportion of the net production may not be consumed until dead, thus becoming the start of a rather different energy flow which we may conveniently designate as the *detritus food chain.* This energy flow takes place largely in the heterotrophic stratum. . . . the detritus energy flow takes place chiefly in the sediments of water systems, and in the litter and soil of land systems.

Ecologists have too often overlooked the fact that the detritus food chain is the more important energy pathway in many ecosystems. . . . a larger portion of net production is estimated to be consumed by grazers in the marine bay than in the forest; nine-tenths of the net production of the forest is estimated to be consumed as detritus (dead leaves, wood, etc.). It is not clear whether this difference is a direct or indirect result of the difference in community structure. One tentative generalization might be proposed as follows: communities of small, rapidly growing producers such as phytoplankton or grass can tolerate heavier grazing pressure than communities of large, slow-growing plants such as trees or large seaweeds. . . .

Despite the large difference in relative size of standing crops in the two extreme types of ecosystems, the actual energy flow may be of the same order of magnitude if light and available nutrients are similar. . . . Thus, 80 KCals of phytoplankton may have a net production almost as large as 5000 KCals of trees (or 500 KCals of green leaves). Therefore, productivity is not proportional to the size of the standing crop except in special cases involving annual plants (as in some agriculture). Unfortunately, many ecologists confuse productivity and standing crop. The relation between structure and function in this case depends on the size and rate of metabolism (and rate of turnover) of the organisms.

To summarize, we see that biological structure influences the pattern of energy flow, particularly the fate of net production and the relative importance of grazers and detritus consumers. However, total energy flow is less affected by structure, and is thus less variable than standing crop. A functional homeostasis has been evolved in nature despite the wide range in species structure and in biomass structure. . . .